C000051945

NORFOLK INTO DANGER – AND BACK

NORFOLK INTO DANGER – AND BACK

Ellen E. Christian

ARTHUR H. STOCKWELL LTD
Torrs Park, Ilfracombe, Devon, EX34 8BA
Established 1898
www.ahstockwell.co.uk

British Library Cataloguing-in-Publication Data.
A catalogue record for this book is available
from the British Library.

ISBN 978-0-7223-4960-1
Printed in Great Britain by
Arthur H. Stockwell Ltd
Torrs Park   Ilfracombe
Devon EX34 8BA

DEDICATION

This book is most respectfully and lovingly dedicated to:

The late Inspector Melvyn (Bill) Ranson, MBE, Metropolitan Police, Holborn Station, and the late Father Barry Carpenter, Cardinal Basil Hume's Chaplin to the Homeless – two wonderfully caring and dedicated human beings, who supported and worked with us often for hours, days and weeks at a time, dealing with many and varied mental health issues, and drug- and alcohol-related illnesses, helping to get vulnerable young and homeless people to safety and on the road to recovery.

Finally, to all those I love, who have supported me on my life's journey – you know who you are.

ACKNOWLEDGEMENTS

My thanks must go to Mr Peter Holland, who gave permission to use the photos in this book, also the *North Norfolk News*, but most of all to my darling Keith for all his help and patience while I have been writing this book.

On Sunday 29 June 1952 at 3.15 p.m. a baby girl, Ellen Elizabeth Lankester, was born weighing five pounds three ounces. This is her story.

CHAPTER 1

It was a beautiful summer day in the Norfolk seaside town of Sheringham. The fishing boats were bobbing up and down on the beautiful blue sea; other fishermen were selling the catches they had brought in earlier in the day while Downtide West and others were mending their nets. It had been a good day for them all.

In a little house down Station Road a new baby cried. Ellen was born into a family where her mum, Rene, was a Salvationist and her dad, Wilfred, was a master butcher. Rene's mum and dad, Jack and Nellie Whall, lived in the town of North Walsham, about eight miles from Sheringham. Rene's younger sister, Audrey, lived with them in a little two-bedroom cottage in Bacton Road. Audrey was twenty-one and so excited at the thought of becoming an auntie she could hardly wait to meet her new niece.

On Monday morning Nellie and Audrey were on the 9-a.m. train to Sheringham to go and meet baby Ellen. They carried beautiful pink and white cardigans knitted by Nellie and Audrey, and the cutest little teddy bear. Grandpa Jack had sent a £5 note. Once Grandma and Auntie Audrey arrived in Sheringham it was just a short walk to the house where they would meet baby Ellen.

The little house was immaculate. The windows sparkled and the red door shone in the morning sunshine. Wilfred greeted them at the front door and ushered them into the hall. The walls were painted pale green; the terracotta tiles gleamed. The rest of the house was very pretty. The front room had flowered wallpaper in various shades of pink and cream; there was a deep-pink three-piece suite, deep-cream curtains and a wooden floor;

there was a fireplace with a cream-and-green tile surround; an oak dresser stood on the back wall with various little ornaments on it. This room was kept for high days and holidays. Pictures hung around the walls. Across the hall was a smaller room with green curtains, two green armchairs, and a small wooden dining table and four chairs. The floor was covered in lino – a room to be used every day. The kitchen had whitewashed walls, a free-standing dresser, a gas cooker, a Belfast sink, a fridge and the luxury of a twin-tub washing machine. There was also an inside toilet. Hanging on the outside wall of the toilet was a tin bath, which was brought in on a Friday night for a bath. Upstairs were three bedrooms, each decorated prettily. One was lemon, one peach, and the smallest bedroom had nursery wallpaper with ducks, rabbits and baby lambs on it. Cream curtains, a wooden cot and a chest of drawers completed the look. All in all this was a very comfortable home.

Grandma and Auntie Audrey ascended the stairs to the bedroom at the front of the house and entered. They found Rene sitting up in bed with the tiniest little baby girl in her arms. Ellen was fast asleep. Auntie Audrey picked her up. Tears filled her eyes.

Audrey's fiancé had died when she was eighteen and she knew she would never have her own child. As she held Ellen she vowed that she would love Ellen for the rest of her life. As Audrey held Ellen, Nellie thought how ill Rene looked. At that moment Wilfred came in with a tray of tea and biscuits. Audrey reluctantly handed Ellen back to Rene to be fed.

After another few hours with Mum and baby, Grandma and Auntie Audrey left with the promise to return the next day. Who knew what the future would hold for Ellen!

As promised, the next afternoon Grandma, Auntie Audrey and Grandpa were back for a visit. As soon as Grandpa saw Ellen no one else could get a look in. Nellie was still concerned as to how ill Rene looked, but Wilfred said the Doctor had said there was no cause for concern, so for the time being Nellie was a little happier.

The rest of the afternoon went by far too quickly. Nellie told

Rene that her elder sister, Kathleen, would be coming from Kent to meet her new niece the next day. Kathleen was a Salvation Army officer and was stationed at a corps in Faversham.

Later that evening Wilfred's mother and father came to see the new baby, said "Oh, she's very sweet" and left.

Rene had a very restless night. By the next morning the Doctor was sent for. Ellen was just a week old. Wilfred found it difficult to cope with a new baby. When Nellie and Kathleen arrived and saw how ill Rene was they decided it would be best if Nellie stayed for a few days, so when Kathleen had met Ellen she would go back to North Walsham and get an overnight bag for Nellie and buy some baby milk as Rene could no longer feed Ellen herself.

Kathleen returned a couple of hours later with Audrey to find Rene very distressed. The Doctor had been sent for. A few minutes later he arrived and said Rene needed to go into hospital.

"We can take the baby," Audrey said. "I will look after her till Rene is well again."

So the Doctor arranged for Rene to go into West Runton hospital the next day. Wilfred had to return to work; Nellie would go with Rene. Audrey and Kathleen would take baby Ellen.

The morning arrived and all was ready. Rene went to hospital with Nellie beside her. She handed her precious baby into Audrey's care. No one knew how long it would be till mother and baby would be reunited. It was Monday 7 July. So much had happened in the week since Ellen had been born. The family were trying to make sense of it all, let alone the adjustment of having a new baby in a small cottage.

The following day news came that Rene had pleurisy and pneumonia and she would be treated with a new penicillin drug. It came as quite a shock to the family that Rene was so ill. Nellie, Jack, Audrey and Kathleen were very concerned, but they put their complete trust in the hospital and believed in the power of prayer and that Rene was in God's hands.

The next morning Kathleen left with the promise of receiving letters as to Rene's progress. The Doctor told Nellie and Jack that Rene might be in hospital for quite some time.

Ellen was a very happy baby, although Audrey was looking after her rather than her mother. Grandpa Jack adored her, taking her out in her pram, and when he went to visit his pals Ellen would go too. A more devoted grandpa you couldn't find.

On the evening of 10 July Jack and Audrey heard a dreadful noise on the stairs. Nellie had fallen from top to bottom and was badly hurt. Dr Holdstock was called for and gave Nellie pain relief with the promise he would be back in the morning. When the Doctor returned the next day he discovered Nellie had had a restless night and her arm had swollen to nearly double its usual size. He wanted to take her to the cottage hospital for an X-ray, but she wouldn't go.

As the weeks went by, Ellen settled into a routine, thriving on all the love she was being given. By the end of July 1952 Ellen had met all ten of her aunts and uncles on Wilfred's side of the family and numerous cousins too.

On Friday 8 August Rene was to be allowed home for the weekend. It was some six weeks since she went into hospital, so it was arranged that Ellen would be dedicated on Sunday the 10th.

Rene arrived home in the early afternoon of Friday looking much better than had been hoped. When Rene was settled in the armchair, Audrey took Ellen from her beautiful Silver Cross pram and placed her in Rene's arms – the first time she had seen her little daughter for six weeks. Tears of joy filled everyone's eyes at the sight of Mum and baby reunited.

At 3 p.m. on Sunday 10 August 1952 Ellen was dedicated at the Salvation Army Hall in Cremer Street in Sheringham. Ellen wore an exquisite christening gown made by Nellie. Rene, Audrey and Kathleen looked very smart in their Salvation Army uniforms; Jack and Wilfred wore suits. It was a lovely service. Afterwards the family returned to the house in Station Road for tea.

Monday came far too soon. Rene returned to hospital. It would be another month before she returned home.

The next few weeks went by without any trouble. News was received from the hospital at regular intervals – Rene was getting stronger by the day.

At the end of August Wilfred was offered a job as manager in Sydney Sexton's butcher's shop in North Walsham, with the promise he could have the two-bedroom flat above the shop. He spoke to Rene and decided he would accept. This would mean they would be only a two-minute walk from Nellie, Jack and Audrey. It was all set for Wilfred to move their home from Sheringham to North Walsham on Monday 1 September 1952. Nellie, Jack and Audrey had thoroughly cleaned the flat and there were new curtains at the windows. It looked and smelt lovely. Audrey had put flowers in the front room and kitchen.

On the morning of 2 September Wilfred opened the shop at 8.30 a.m. and was surprised to find a queue outside. The customers on the whole were friendly and waited patiently to be served, handing over their ration books. It was a busy day. At 6 p.m. Wilfred closed the shop, washed all the counters down and went upstairs to the flat, tired but content.

Great news: Rene was coming home on 9 September. She had made a full recovery. At last Rene, Wilfred and Ellen would be a family. Ellen was ten weeks old.

Wilfred borrowed a car and set off to bring Rene home. Nellie and Audrey prepared tea in the flat. Jack took Ellen out in the pram. After what seemed like forever, Rene was home. She loved the flat. They waited a few minutes till Jack brought Ellen back. Rene couldn't believe how much Ellen had changed in ten weeks. Her grey-green eyes sparkled; her hair was light brown and shone. Rene thought she was the most beautiful baby in the world.

After tea Nellie, Jack and Audrey said their goodbyes till the next day. The day had been a good one.

CHAPTER 2

The next few months passed by pleasantly enough as autumn turned to winter. By December 1952 Ellen was almost six months old – a very friendly child who delighted everyone except her dad. He found it very difficult to cope with a young child, so once more Auntie Audrey stepped in, taking Ellen two or three days a week. As they were now living in North Walsham, Rene was able to see Ellen every day.

As Christmas of 1952 approached Wilfred was very busy in the shop. It was full of every cut of meat and poultry you could imagine. Turkeys, pheasants and rabbits hung from hooks; salt beef was soaking in the brine tub in the corner. There was a dressed boar's head in the centre of the display in the window with an apple in its mouth.

Rene spent far more time at her childhood home in Bacton Road, often returning home just in time to prepare the evening meal.

Everyone awoke on Christmas Day to a thick covering of snow. The children loved it, but not the grown-ups. Everywhere looked so very pretty, but people hoped it wouldn't last – except the children, who were having great fun with snowball fights in the street and hitting the odd passer-by.

Mr Edwards was heard shouting, "Bloomin' kids want a clip o' the lug!" as his trilby went flying off his head.

In January 1953 the snow continued to fall. It was difficult to get around. Neighbours looked after each other and everyone made the best of the situation.

By the end of February there was still no let-up in the

weather. Eight-month-old Ellen delighted in watching the snowflakes with her devoted Grandpa. As March approached Nellie became unwell. Dr Holdstock came, and this time insisted that Nellie have a thorough check-up at the cottage hospital. She agreed reluctantly, so on Friday 6 March Nellie went for her appointment.

Ten days later, on 16 March, Dr Holdstock came to the cottage in Bacton Road with the news that Nellie had cancer and it was quite advanced. What a shock for the family! Dr Holdstock assured them that he would do everything in his power for Nellie.

The next few weeks seemed unreal as the family tried to make sense of what they had been told. Audrey was now running the home while still looking after Ellen three days a week. Rene visited every day to help and take care of Nellie. Ellen continued to be adored by her grandpa, and he often said that Ellen was keeping him sane.

On the morning of Friday 22 August Nellie was extremely poorly. Nothing more could be done. She went to heaven in her sleep on Saturday 30 August. Little Ellen was just fourteen months old.

A week later Nellie's funeral service was held at the Salvation Army Hall in Hall Lane. It was full. After the service Nellie was laid to rest in the town cemetery in Bacton Road.

Life continued for the family as Jack, Rene, Kathleen and Audrey adjusted. 1953 was coming to an end and Wilfred and Rene had been offered a little house with a garden in Mundesley Road, North Walsham. Rene thought it would be lovely to have a garden as it would be good for Ellen. They accepted, decorated the house and made the small bedroom into a nursery. It was painted lemon, and one wall had Noddy wallpaper. Deep-lemon curtains were hung at the windows. Rene desperately wanted her little daughter home, and hoped Wilfred would come to love her too.

In the second week of March 1954 the Lankester family moved into the house. Life was good. Ellen was walking and talking and getting up to mischief.

One afternoon, on a visit to her grandpa, Rene, Audrey and Jack were having a cup of tea. Ellen had toddled off. They heard giggling coming from the scullery, and on investigation they found Ellen sitting with the dog in the coal hole. They couldn't help but laugh – a little girl in a pink dress that was now black and a spaniel that was no longer cream. They were both washed – Ellen in the kitchen sink and the dog in the tin bath outside. Grandpa Jack put a lock on the coal-hole door.

Several happy months went by and the family all came together for Ellen's third birthday on 29 June 1955. Mum and Dad gave Ellen a doll, Auntie Audrey had knitted two lovely little cardigans, Auntie Kathleen sent a toy pink rabbit and Grandpa Jack had started a bank account with £30 at the Penny Bank in town. He would add to it over the following years. Wilfred seemed to be coping a bit better with Ellen, although he only saw her for a short time each evening. But for now Rene was happy.

Now that Ellen was three, Rene decided she was old enough to go to the Sunday school. She loved it. She sang in her own little way and had a small tambourine, which she loved, making as much noise as possible. It could not be said that Ellen was a quiet child.

After Sunday school Rene and Audrey stayed for the 11-a.m. service. Rene wanted to see how well Ellen would behave. She needn't have worried – Ellen sat in her pushchair as good as gold. She thought the band was wonderful. When Rene and Audrey sang in the Songsters she clapped her hands.

At twelve noon the service ended. Audrey and Rene went home for lunch, saying that they would meet at the hall for Sunday school once more. Rene would take Ellen again and the three of them would stay for the 3-p.m. service.

At four thirty, when Rene returned home for tea, Wilfred wasn't too happy that his wife spent all day at the Salvation Army, each and every Sunday. Nevertheless Rene returned for the 6-p.m. service and the 7-p.m. prayer meeting. Rene left Ellen in Wilfred's care.

When Rene returned home shortly after 8 p.m. she went

upstairs to change out of her uniform. She then looked in on Ellen. What a sight met her eyes! Wilfred had put Ellen in her cot in a lovely white nightgown. He had given her some paper, a pencil and blue carbon paper. The sheets, covers and Ellen were covered in bright-blue pigment.

Ellen looked up at Rene and said, "Pretty Mummy."

Rene smiled at her little daughter.

After she had given her a bath and changed her cot she went downstairs to Wilfred.

"What were you thinking?" she said. "Ellen could have eaten that paper."

He replied, "You shouldn't have left her."

Over the next few weeks it became clear that Wilfred was having difficulties once again with Ellen.

At the end of November 1955 Wilfred's parents passed away. Wilfred's ten brothers and sisters all attended the funerals.

As another Christmas approached Audrey suggested the family all go to Bacton Road for Christmas Day. This was agreed and preparations were made. As Wilfred had a very generous weekly meat allowance from the shop he would provide Audrey with a turkey, ham joint, sausages and bacon. Some of the vegetables would come from Grandpa's garden. Audrey made the cake and Rene made the pudding. On Christmas Eve, when Ellen had gone to bed, Rene decorated a small Christmas tree in the front room; at the same time Audrey was also putting a tree in her front room, and presents were put under the tree ready for Ellen the following day. The turkey and ham were cooked and in the pantry, which was so cold ice formed on the inside of the window; the veg had been prepared and put in bowls of cold water and ice was forming on the top. Thus everything was ready.

Snow lay thick on the ground as Rene woke Ellen that Christmas morning.

When Ellen saw the tree she clapped her hands and said, "Pretty Tismas."

Beneath the tree were a wooden jigsaw puzzle of a farm

scene, a box of coloured bricks and *The Three Bears Storybook*. Rene had saved up and had bought Ellen a beautiful red velvet dress for her to wear; she had knitted a white cardigan and also bought white socks and black patent-leather shoes.

After breakfast Rene, Wilfred and Ellen walked the three minutes to Bacton Road. When they walked into the kitchen the smell of a delicious meal greeted them. Immediately Ellen ran to her beloved Grandy, as she was now calling Jack. He scooped her up in his arms. No one could love a child more.

Once a cup of tea was made there were more presents to open – a doll from Auntie Audrey and a spinning top from Grandy. He had also put £40 in her bank account, and there were two Noddy books from Auntie Kathleen. There was much laughter when Rene and Audrey opened their gifts to each other. They had both knitted pink cardigans in exactly the same colour and pattern. Kathleen had knitted socks for her dad and a scarf for Wilfred, and for each sister she had sent a cream blouse.

At 1 p.m. lunch was served. It was lovely – turkey, stuffing, roast and mashed potatoes, cauliflower, runner beans, carrots and sprouts, with onion gravy. Ellen had taken a dislike to meat of any kind except sausages, so Audrey had done some especially for Ellen.

She loved veg, so that wasn't a problem to anyone but Wilfred, who said, "She's the daughter of a butcher – she will do as she is told and eat some meat, even if I have to feed her."

This outburst upset Ellen and she tried to hide behind Grandy.

He said to Wilfred, "Leave the child alone – what does it matter?" He turned and looked at Ellen and said, "Come and sit near Grandy and eat your dinner and we'll say nothing more about it."

Audrey and Rene didn't like what they had seen and heard either.

After lunch was over, Ellen played happily with her new toys and Grandy read one of her Noddy books to her. Jack had bought a television earlier in the year, so the family listened to the Queen's speech on the BBC at 3 p.m. At three fifteen there was a visit to Disneyland and at four forty-five *Watch with Mother*.

Christmas Day tea was ham or tinned-salmon sandwiches, trifle and Christmas cake or mince pies. At 7 p.m. on ITV there was a carol service from Paddington Children's Hospital. At seven forty-five *Sunday Night at the London Palladium* was on, which Grandy slept through. Ellen was also fast asleep, so it was decided that she would be taken upstairs to bed and stay with Audrey until the next day.

Rene and Wilfred said goodnight at around 10 p.m. and headed off home. The snow was falling heavily, so they were glad they had their wellingtons. It continued to snow all night and by Boxing Day morning they were snowed in. Most of the town was cut off, but still neighbour tried to help neighbour. It continued to snow all day. Everywhere was eerily quiet.

By Tuesday the 27th Wilfred had managed to dig a path from the front door so he could get into town to open the shop. Meanwhile Rene decided to try and walk down Bacton Road to visit Audrey and Jack. It was hard work, but she made it. Audrey was busy making two turkey-and-veg pies. She was a wonderful cook and could make something tasty out of almost anything. Rene noticed a snowman in the garden wearing one of Jack's caps and with a pipe in its mouth. She was sure Grandy and Ellen had something to do with it, and of course she was right.

Rene spent a pleasant few hours with Audrey, Jack and Ellen. When Rene got ready to leave she went to put Ellen's coat on.

The child cried, "No – no like Daddy. Stay Audy's house with Grandy."

Audrey and Rene could not believe what they heard. The child was obviously frightened of her father. Both sisters looked at Ellen sitting on Grandy's knee, crying.

Jack said in his broad Norfolk accent, "Now, stop you a-cryin' and we can talk to Mummy."

No one was going to upset his Ellen.

Jack suggested that with Ellen being so upset she should

stay with him and Audrey, and Rene would talk to Wilfred. So once more Ellen was in Audrey's care. Rene left the cottage with a turkey-and-veg pie for dinner and a very heavy heart.

When Wilfred came home that evening Rene gave him his dinner, washed up and put everything away. She then went into the small sitting room, sat in an armchair and began knitting.

They sat in silence until he said, "Is she in bed, then?" When Rene told him what had happened earlier in the day and that Ellen had been upset, so she was staying with Jack and Audrey so they could talk, he said, "Jack ruins that child and Audrey gives in all the time. While she lives in my house she will do as she is told."

Rene said that she loved her little daughter and wanted her to be happy.

Wilfred said, "If she lives here she will do as I say. If you can't deal with that then leave her with Audrey. I won't stop you seeing her, but you will look after this home and prepare my meals. Make up your mind – no child will rule me."

1955 was not ending happily.

CHAPTER 3

At the beginning of January 1956 Rene went to see Jack, Audrey and Ellen. While Jack kept an eye on Ellen, Rene told Audrey what Wilfred had said. Audrey was horrified. Ellen was such a happy, well-behaved little girl. After much talking, Jack agreed with Audrey and Rene that Ellen would live with Audrey and Grandy; Rene would see her every day.

Over the next few months Ellen began to blossom. By the time she was four years old, in June, she was beginning to read simple children's books, and could count up to 100 and recite the alphabet. She loved to sing and was going to the Salvation Army on a Sunday with Rene and Audrey. Jack continued to dote on his only grandchild. He often thought how Nellie would have loved her.

One Saturday there was to be an evening band and Songster concert at the hall. Kathleen was back home for the weekend, so she would go along with Audrey and Ellen and meet Rene at the hall. Audrey got Ellen ready in a little white dress, pink cardigan, white socks and white sandals. Kathleen was in her uniform. As it was a lovely evening Ellen and Kathleen waited in the garden. It should be known at this point in our story that Audrey kept six ducks and a drake at the bottom of the garden, which was fenced off with a low fence of chicken wire. There was a pond made from an old sunken tin bath, and an old Belfast sink was used for food. On this particular day there was mashed potato, bread, beetroot and duck meal in the sink and the pond had been filled that morning.

Ellen said, "Auntie Nassie run!"

Kathleen was more than happy to play with her little niece. They were having a lovely time. Then, as they ran around the corner a bit too quickly, they both fell straight into the sink with Kathleen's arm in the duck pond. They looked a sight. Ellen's dress was covered in dirt and beetroot, as was Kathleen's uniform. There were, however, squeals of laughter as they both sat there. The back door of the cottage opened and out came Audrey and Jack. Their faces were a picture. Kathleen and Ellen sat there laughing, surrounded by the ducks.

Audrey said, "What on earth are you two doing? Look at you!"

This caused more laughter, and Jack joined in.

Audrey said to Ellen, "Get indoors, in the kitchen. Kathleen, you should know better." Then as she looked at her sister and her niece she began laughing too.

What an auntie!

Once Kathleen and Ellen were cleaned up, the three of them set off for the hall, with just a few minutes to spare, leaving Jack to mend the fence.

Rene said to Audrey, "Why are you late?"

Audrey said, "Don't ask!" and smiled.

As 1956 came to a close Rene was far happier, but secretly she wondered what the future would hold. With Jack, Audrey and her sister Kathleen she could cope. Rene had a firm belief that her life was in God's hands and that her life was planned.

1957 started well and Ellen was to start school at Easter. Ellen was excited, but Jack knew he would miss her. On Monday 29 April Ellen started school dressed in a navy pinafore dress, a white blouse, a red cardigan that her mum had knitted, white socks and black shoes. Over these she had on a grey coat with a red velvet collar. Grandy had tears in his eyes as he waved her goodbye.

Rene walked the five minutes to school with Ellen, happy to find she recognised some of the other mums who brought their children to Sunday school. Several of them spoke to Rene and some of the children came running over to Ellen. Most of the children seemed happy at the prospect of starting school. When the teacher rang the bell at 9 a.m. sharp the children all lined up neatly and walked in one by one – all that is except one little girl called Pauline. She hung on to her mummy, and the teacher, Miss Rump, had to take her by the hand, screaming.

Once inside school, the children watched wide-eyed as Pauline lay on the floor screaming and kicking, shouting, "I'll scream and scream until I'm sick." And she did.

Pauline did this every day until she was nine years old.

Oh, how Ellen hated school! She had to be quiet and sit still, and on two occasions she had to stand in the corner.

Once when the teacher asked her to put a book down she was reading, Ellen said, "No, I haven't finished."

The teacher asked her again.

Ellen replied, "Shan't."

The second time Ellen ran out of the classroom to go to the toilet.

Ellen ate her lunch and after that the lesson was arithmetic. Ellen added two plus two and three plus three, but she got cross when she couldn't subtract two from five.

At 3 p.m. Rene collected her little daughter, and when asked if she'd had a nice day Ellen replied, "No, I won't come back."

Little did she realise she would have to go back for the next ten years.

During the next few months although Ellen disliked school with a vengeance she settled into a routine.

Rene continued to keep busy when Ellen was at school, looking after her home in Mundesley Road and at the weekend going to the Salvation Army with Audrey and Ellen.

At Christmas Ellen was given just two presents, including a beautiful Silver Cross doll's pram just like the one she had as a baby. Rene had made lovely pink and lemon covers for it. Rene had saved all year. It had cost £28 and ten shillings. Inside the pram sat a life-size china baby doll dressed in lemon and white. Grandy had bought the doll and Audrey had knitted the doll's clothes. Ellen was so excited.

After lunch on Christmas Day there was a knock at the

cottage door. It was Kathleen, who had managed to get away unexpectedly. Everyone was thrilled to see her.

"Oh! My Nassie here," said Ellen. She couldn't say Kathleen when she started talking and called her Nassie. From then on it remained.

Kathleen brought a bag in with her. Inside it were two lovely little dresses for Ellen along with a children's Bible.

The day went very well and, as Wilfred had seemed in a better frame of mind, Rene thought it would be OK if Ellen stayed with him and Rene overnight. Jack wasn't so sure.

The next morning all was well. After breakfast Ellen played happily with her new pram and doll, and later in the day the family would all be together in Bacton Road for Boxing Day tea. 1957 ended on a happy note.

1958 began well. Ellen was thriving and made some nice little friends at school and the Salvation Army. One of her little friends from school lived two houses down from Audrey, so they often played together. Although Ellen still disliked school she loved learning. Rene and Audrey continued to take Ellen to the Salvation Army every Sunday. Life was very pleasant for all the family. Jack missed his little granddaughter so much, but at least she was happy.

As 1958 turned into 1959 all was well.

In the spring of 1959 Kathleen heard that in May she would be moving to Wales. She was to be the officer in charge of the Cwm Corps of the Salvation Army (officers usually move every three to five years). Audrey told Ellen that, if she continued to be a good girl, in the school summer holidays they would go on a train and have a holiday with Kathleen. Ellen was so excited. Audrey told her that they would have to go on three trains, but for now they must wait.

School seemed to go on forever, then at last the summer holidays began. On the morning of 14 July, after saying goodbye to Rene and Grandy, Audrey and Ellen walked the ten minutes to North Walsham Station to catch the 10-a.m. train to Norwich. They arrived in Norwich at 11.50 a.m. ready to board the noon train to London. Soon they were on their way. Ellen loved the journey and watching the scenery go by. They had tea on the train. Ellen thought it great fun when the ticket inspector punched a hole in her ticket, and she giggled when the train's whistle blew.

At 4.50 p.m. they arrived in London at Euston Station. Audrey's friend Mary was waiting for them. Mary's husband, Fred, had a car, so he would take them to his and Mary's house in St John's Wood, where they would stay overnight. Ellen was thrilled at being in a car, and felt very important as she was allowed to sit in the front. Mary had put a cushion on the seat so Ellen could see where they were going.

When they arrived at Mary's, Audrey thought the house was lovely. It was much bigger than her home in Norfolk. It had two sitting rooms, a large kitchen big enough to eat in and a downstairs toilet. Upstairs there were four bedrooms and a bathroom. Ellen was amazed to find she could have a bath without boiling the copper and bringing in the tin bath as she did at home.

She said to Mary, "Will I get drowned in there?"

Mary said, "There's no need to worry."

Audrey loved Mary's house, but she wasn't jealous or envious. She adored her little cottage in Norfolk, full of love.

Once they had finished their dinner of sausage, mash, peas, carrots and gravy, Ellen had a bath and went to bed and fell asleep almost immediately.

It was when Mary, Fred and Audrey were having a cup of tea that Mary suggested that when Audrey and Ellen came back from Kathleen's they could stay for a few days so Mary could take them to see some of the sights of London.

Audrey said, "Oh, yes, please. Ellen would love it, but I won't tell her – I will keep it as a surprise."

With that, Audrey said goodnight, had a bath and went to bed.

The following morning Audrey and Ellen got the train to

Wales. Mary had given them a packed lunch and drinks for the journey – enough to feed an army. It would take seven hours. It was a lovely sunny day and time seemed to go by quickly. Before they knew it they saw Kathleen waiting on the platform in Cwm. It was a short bus ride to Kathleen's – a small two-bedroom house at the bottom of a huge mountain. Ellen was surprised to see enormous mountains of coal. There were horses and sheep roaming freely, and she thought it was wonderful. It was 9 p.m., so after something to eat and drink it was time for bed. It had been such an exciting day.

The next morning was bright and sunny, so after breakfast Audrey and Ellen were going for a walk up the mountain while Kathleen went to visit an elderly lady.

All at once Audrey and Kathleen heard a scream. They ran outside and found Ellen in the outside toilet surrounded by sheep. Kathleen and Audrey laughed, and after a minute or two Ellen laughed too. Ellen had seen sheep many times before, but not this close. Over the next few days she became used to it.

Audrey, Ellen and Kathleen went their separate ways with the promise of meeting back at the house at 1 p.m. for lunch. Ellen loved climbing up the mountain and took great delight in rolling back down again. Audrey loved the stillness and the little streams that rippled quietly by. They saw the massive wheel of a coal mine and a little train of thirty wagons full of coal. Ellen counted every one.

The next month passed by very pleasantly. Audrey and Kathleen would sit in the pretty little garden and chat while Ellen played with the little girl next door. Her name was Bronwyn. She was about three months older than Ellen.

On the Sundays they were on holiday, they went to Cwm Corps, where Kathleen was in charge. Audrey said that she had never heard such wonderful singers as the Welsh people, with their lovely lilting accent. Sometimes it sounded as if they were singing when they spoke.

Before Audrey and Ellen left North Walsham, Grandy had

given Ellen a whole £5 just for her to spend. Ellen bought a doll in Welsh costume, a handkerchief with a Welsh dragon on it for her mum and a pencil that said 'Wales' on it for Grandy.

She said, "That's just what Grandy needs."

All too soon it was time to leave Kathleen and Wales and head back to London to Mary and Fred, who were waiting for them once again. Once back at Mary's house Audrey told Ellen they were going to stay with Mary and Fred for a few days. Ellen could barely contain her excitement. After a lovely meal the friends sat down to chat.

The following morning after breakfast Fred left for work. He was a policeman. He let Ellen try on his helmet and he looked very smart in his uniform.

A short while later Mary, Audrey and Ellen caught the bus. First of all they went to Trafalgar Square, where they fed the pigeons and saw Nelson's Column. Then they walked up the Mall to Buckingham Palace. Ellen thought she ought to wave just in case the Queen was looking out of the window.

After lunch Mary surprised Ellen when she said they were going to London Zoo. Ellen squealed with delight, so off they went on another bus. Once in the zoo, they saw some parrots that had been trained to ride a tiny bicycle and to push a tiny pram. Next it was off to see the penguins being fed, swimming under the water to get the fish. They met Guy the gorilla and Chi Chi the panda, but Ellen thought seeing Brumas the polar bear was the best of all. Before they left the zoo they went into the shop and Mary bought Ellen a Brumas bear toy.

"Oh, Auntie Mary, thank you," she said.

They had enjoyed such a wonderful day.

When they got back to Mary's Ellen wrote on the postcard she had bought for Grandy. It had Buckingham Palace on it. Ellen would post it the next day, and Mary gave her a twopenny stamp for it.

The next day Fred didn't have to go to work, so they all went out in his car. First they went to Kew Gardens. Audrey was thrilled at the beautiful flowers, especially the roses. Later in the day they had a boat trip on the Thames from the

Embankment to Tower Bridge. By the end of the day everyone was happy but exhausted.

On Friday 11 September it was time to leave Mary and Fred. They said goodbye, got the bus to the station and boarded the train at 10 a.m. The journey was very pleasant and they arrived in Norwich at 2.55 p.m. There was a little wait for the train to North Walsham, so Audrey and Ellen had a drink. When the train came into the station for three thirty they boarded it, and arrived back in North Walsham an hour later. It was just a short walk home. When they left to go on holiday they had just one suitcase; now they had two. One was borrowed from Kathleen.

Ellen ran into the little cottage in Bacton Road, straight into Grandy's arms. He was so pleased to have them home. Rene would be down the following morning.

CHAPTER 4

On Saturday morning Audrey got up early to do some washing and baking for the following week. Once the washing was on the line, Audrey went into town to go to the grocer and butcher. She left Ellen with Jack. While she was in town Audrey bought a chicken, minced beef, two onions, sugar, eggs and cheese, also five pounds of potatoes.

She met Rene in Woolworth's, so they walked back to Bacton Road together. Rene said that everything at home was good and that she and Wilfred had been offered a council house in Morris Road, about a twenty-minute walk from town. It had two bedrooms, much bigger than they had now, a large lounge, a good-size kitchen with a walk-in pantry, and a very nice bathroom. They had decided to take it. The council would have it cleaned and would decorate it throughout with magnolia walls and white paintwork. It would be ready for them to move into by the end of October.

Audrey was pleased for her sister, but she wondered how this would be for Ellen. Would she be expected to move in with Rene and Wilfred? She needn't have been concerned, as Rene asked Ellen what she wanted to do. She said, "Stay with my Audy and Grandy." So for now everyone was happy.

On 12 October Rene and Wilfred moved into Morris Road. As Christmas 1959 approached, the family prepared to spend Christmas at Rene and Wilfred's. It turned out to be a wonderful time.

1960 began well, and by the middle of March Ellen went to

live with Rene and Wilfred once more. Jack had said that it was on the condition that if Ellen wasn't happy she should go back to Audrey.

All was fine, so on Ellen's eighth birthday Rene gave her a party. It was a glorious sunny day, so it was held in the garden after school. There were eight of Ellen's little friends from school and the Salvation Army. Audrey and Grandy came too. There were hot dogs, chips, jelly and ice cream and a birthday cake in the form of a pink-and-white number eight. Grandy and Audrey bought Ellen a shiny black bicycle with a little basket on the front. Audrey promised to take Ellen for a bicycle ride on the Saturday. Rene had given Ellen a beautiful doll's house. It had eight rooms, all with the tiniest furniture inside, and with little curtains at the windows. There was also a family of four dolls – Mum, Dad, a boy and a girl. It had been put in the second bedroom in the hope that Ellen would stay at Morris Road. She also received two books, another doll, some sweets, a colouring book and crayons, and a knitting set.

That evening as Audrey and Jack went home they thought that their Ellen was happy and safe.

On Saturday morning, as promised, Audrey came to take Ellen for her bicycle ride. As it was such a lovely day Audrey had packed a picnic and a towel. She thought it would be nice to cycle to Mundesley, about four miles away, to have a picnic on the beach and a paddle in the sea. So off they went. Ellen had put Teddy in the basket on the front of the bicycle. She said that he would like the seaside. Ellen did very well on her bicycle, but sometimes Audrey would put her hand on Ellen's shoulder and help her along. Oh, how Ellen loved her!

When they arrived in Mundesley they parked their bicycles at Mr Payne's tea shop, got an ice cream and went on to the beach. Audrey paid tuppence for two deckchairs. After a little while Audrey watched as Ellen went for a paddle in the warm blue sea with her dress tucked into her knickers. It was turning into a lovely day for auntie and niece. The sun was shining and the sea was as calm as a millpond. Nothing could spoil Audrey's contentment.

At 5.30 p.m. the two of them set off for home. When they got back to North Walsham Ellen stopped to see Grandy and to give him the two shiny pebbles she had picked up from the beach. Of course he thought they were the loveliest pebbles he had ever seen. Audrey took Ellen back to Rene at 8 p.m., in time for bed. Rene told Audrey that her back was hurting, but she had not said anything to Wilfred.

The following morning Rene was still having trouble with her back. She did not want to miss going to the Salvation Army, so reluctantly Wilfred said that he would take her and Ellen in the van. Rene suggested she should stay at Audrey's as it was close to the hall and that he should come to Audrey's for lunch and then pick her and Ellen up later. Amazingly, he agreed.

Audrey, Rene and Ellen were at the Salvation Army all day, and at 8.30 p.m. Wilfred picked Rene and Ellen up. Ellen was in her pyjamas, ready for bed.

On Monday morning Rene's back was so bad she couldn't get out of bed. Wilfred asked the neighbour to sit with her while he took Ellen to school and to fetch the Doctor and Audrey. Dr Holdstock said he would be there as soon as possible.

Audrey went straight up to Rene's and had only been there two minutes before the Doctor arrived. After seeing Rene, he went to arrange an ambulance to take Rene to the cottage hospital. He told Audrey not to worry – he would let her know what Rene's diagnosis was. On her way home, Audrey went into the shop to tell Wilfred and said that she would keep Ellen at Bacton Road for the time being.

Later in the afternoon Dr Holdstock called in on Jack and Audrey to say that Rene had severe lumbago and would be home the following day. "Have a bed brought downstairs, and she must have complete bed rest," he advised.

Audrey went to tell Wilfred, and he said that he would bring a single bed down out of Ellen's room.

Audrey then went to see one of Rene's friends and asked if she would sit with Rene, prepare a meal for her and do a little housework. Audrey told her she could take her baby with her and Wilfred would pay her £3 and five shillings a week.

The arrangements were agreed as Rene's friend had lost her husband in a motorcycle accident when her baby daughter was just seven months old and she couldn't go to work as all her family lived away in Scotland. Once again Ellen was in Audrey and Jack's care.

When Rene came home from hospital the front room looked very pretty. Margaret had picked some roses from the garden and put them on a small table by the bed, which had a pretty green-and-lemon bedspread and snowy-white cotton sheets and pillowcases. Dr Holdstock had insisted that a wooden board, which he had delivered the day before, should be put under the mattress.

After school Audrey and Ellen came to see Rene. Ellen couldn't understand why Rene couldn't give her a hug. They tried to explain to no avail.

Ellen said, "Don't care – Grandy loves me."

The next few weeks were hard for Rene. All she could really do was read or knit. She could not get in or out of the bath and had to have a good wash instead with Margaret's help. Audrey would come and visit every day, but Ellen didn't want to so she stayed with Jack or played with her friends.

After three months Rene was a little better and managing on fewer painkillers. Summer turned into autumn, and one more Christmas came and went without incident.

By the March of 1961 Rene had completely recovered. However, Ellen was not to go back to Morris Road. Weekends were still spent at the Salvation Army. Now that Ellen was nine years old, Rene had insisted that Ellen should join the Singing Company (children's choir) and the Timbrel Group (tambourine). It soon became clear that Ellen had a beautiful singing voice, so Rene sent her to singing lessons. Very quickly Ellen realised that she would have very little time for her non-Army friends as she spent all day Sunday at the Salvation Army. Monday was timbrel practice from 6 p.m. to 7 p.m.; Tuesday was Singing Company practice from 4 p.m. till 5 p.m. On Wednesdays after school Ellen was allowed half an hour with her non-Army friends. Thursday was Bible study and on Friday Ellen went to singing lessons from six thirty until seven thirty. By the time she got home she was so tired she went straight to bed. This routine continued even in the school holidays, and it was even worse when the Sunday school were practising for anniversary celebrations or the Christmas play. Ellen was expected to learn two new recitations word perfect, and two solos. It was no good complaining, so she just got on with it, often resenting this regime – especially when her friends asked her to tea or asked her to go out with them at the weekends and Ellen had to say no.

Jack didn't agree with any of this and occasionally said, "I'm going to take Ellen out on Sunday – it will do the child good."

They would catch the train to Great Yarmouth in the summer, and in the winter they would sit indoors together reading or playing dominoes. This time with Grandy became very precious to Ellen.

It was January 1962. Ellen was growing up and would soon be ten years old. No one could say what the next few years would hold. By now it had been decided that Ellen would live with Audrey and Jack permanently. She found it far too difficult to live with Wilfred, but Rene continued to see her most days. The Salvation Army routine became the norm and Ellen accepted it, although she didn't like it. Life went on from day to day.

Ellen's tenth birthday arrived. She was allowed to take three friends – Susan, Linda and Marilyn – to the cinema to see *Jack and the Beanstalk*. The cinema was on New Road in North Walsham. Grandy had given Ellen half a crown so that the four girls could stop at Payne's sweet shop and get a quarter pound of sweets each. There would be enough left over for an ice cream in the interval. Audrey walked up New Road with the girls. She went into the cinema and paid the threepence for each of the girls to go upstairs. As it was Friday the girls had been allowed to go to the evening show. They felt very grown-up.

When the film had finished, Audrey and Linda and Marilyn's

dads were waiting for the girls. Susan would walk home with Ellen and Audrey. After Linda and Marilyn had thanked Audrey, the friends parted company and went home.

When they got back to Bacton Road Audrey and Ellen walked two doors from home to make sure Susan was OK. Susan gave Auntie Audrey a hug and the friends said goodnight.

The following morning, being Saturday, Grandy took Ellen into town for her week's supply of sweets. Their first stop was Mrs Oakley's, where Grandy got his ounce of Old Holborn pipe tobacco. Jack also bought a quarter of rum-and-butter toffees and a quarter of mint humbugs. He also bought a Fry's Five Boys chocolate bar for Audrey. Ellen chose a penny toffee strip and two ounces of Dolly Mixtures. The next stop was Sid Salmon's bicycle shop for a puncture repair kit. Audrey's bicycle had a puncture on the front wheel. Next it was Jeary's, where Ellen chose two gobstoppers and a sherbet dip.

Grandy and Ellen then went into the butcher's to buy some sausages, bacon and a chicken for Sunday lunch. Wilfred still had a generous meat allowance, so Jack only had to pay for the bacon. Wilfred was very civil to Jack and came from behind the counter to give Ellen a hug. Finally it was into Arnold Pitcher's for Grandy's *Eastern Daily Press* and Ellen's *Jackie* magazine.

If Audrey had known what happened next she would have had a fit! Jack took Ellen into the White Swan to have half a pint with some of his friends from the Forget-Me-Not Club. Jack had his usual stout. Ellen had a juice, but she loved it when Grandy let her have a sip of his drink.

Percy said to Jack in broad Norfolk, "Dorn't you let that gal Audrey catch you bringin' the little 'un in here. She won't half holler."

Jack laughed. His pals loved Ellen and she loved going out with Grandy on a Saturday.

After about an hour they walked home to Bacton Road, where Audrey had lunch ready.

"Where have you two been?" she asked.

Ellen replied, "In the Swan."

"Oh, Dad, you know I don't like her going in the pub."
(Salvationists are completely teetotal.)

Jack said, "That won't hurt her."

Audrey walked away, smiling.

The rest of the day was pleasant enough. Rene came down after lunch and took Ellen to the park, and when they came home at four thirty Ellen was worn out.

After tea the tin bath was brought indoors. The copper in the corner of the kitchen had been on for a while, so the water was nice and hot. Although it was a summer day a fire had been lit in the small sitting room and the tin bath was put in front of it. The wooden clothes horse was put up with a sheet over it to give a little privacy when having a bath. Once the bath had been filled, Audrey sprinkled some lavender bath salts into the water. Ellen was first in, then Audrey and finally Jack. Once when Ellen was in the bath the dog jumped in too. Ellen thought it was great fun.

Later in the evening Audrey, Jack and Ellen watched *Come Dancing* on the television, compèred by Peter West.

The next day, being Sunday, was spent at the Salvation Army ALL DAY! The children in Sunday school were told they were going to present a BIG Christmas play and that practices would begin at the end of July. There was a combined heartfelt sigh. There were over 100 children, and Mrs Warnes (the Sunday-school superintendent) said that every child would have a part, no matter how young they were.

Over the next few weeks the children chatted among themselves, discussing what parts they would be given, hoping they wouldn't have too many lines to learn. Mrs Warnes insisted that the children were word-perfect for all the plays and anniversary celebrations. Three weeks later the parts were given out. Many of the children were happy they only had a few lines to learn, but the older children, including Ellen, couldn't believe what they saw. Three of the older boys would be the kings. David was to play Joseph. Barry would be the innkeeper. There were to be several shepherds. Marilyn would be the Angel Gabriel and there would be many other angels.

Then Ellen looked at the paper in her hand. She was horrified. She was to play King Herod at the start of the play. There was a very big part to learn for that. She would also play Mary. She had to learn two songs – 'Little Donkey' and 'Mary's Boy Child' – which she would sing as solos plus the recitation 'On the Road to Bethlehem'. She could have cried. She felt her life in the next few months would be nothing but school, Salvation Army and music lessons. It was a lot for a little girl of ten to take in. For many of the other Salvationists' children it was much the same. In the sixties children didn't argue with their parents. It was just accepted, although at times reluctantly.

The next few months were very busy. Ellen was learning her lines and songs, as were the other children. The Sunday-school teachers were making costumes for the kings, Joseph and the Angel Gabriel. Rene was very busy making angels' wings. Gabriel's were gold and beautiful; the other wings – all forty of them – were white and silver. Rene had cut out individual tissue-paper feathers and they looked stunning. Ellen's friend had been a bridesmaid the year previous and Ellen would borrow her blue dress for Mary. Her Herod costume was being made. There would be twenty-two shepherds, who would wear dressing gowns with tea towels on their heads. Everything was coming together.

All at once the day for the dress rehearsal arrived. There would be four performances of the play in mid December – two at the secondary school on Manor Road and two at the Salvation Army Hall. The dress rehearsal went very well. All the children remembered their lines. Ellen's solos were lovely, as was her recitation. Two little girls sang a duet of 'Frosty the Snowman'. One little boy played the cornet and the youngest children – between three and six years old – sang 'Away in a Manger'. The forty angels and Gabriel looked wonderful with white dresses, and the wings were a sight to behold. When they sang 'Silent Night' there wasn't a dry eye to be seen. Mrs Warnes praised all the children and told them that all the tickets had been sold – 250 for each performance at the school and 200 for the performances at the Salvation Army Hall.

At last the two big days arrived. The children were getting ready backstage at the school – except for Ellen, who would be first onstage to sing her first solo, 'Little Donkey'. Audrey had bought her a lovely new dress. It was pale blue with a silver thread running through it. Mr Gee would accompany Ellen on the piano.

Ellen was so excited as Grandy was coming to all four performances. Rene told Wilfred that he would be expected to attend one of the performances, and he said that he would go to one at the Salvation Army Hall.

Some of the children peeped from behind the curtain and were surprised that the school hall was full. There were some of their schoolteachers, and the headmaster was there, as was the mayor and Uncle Ted, the town policeman – a man the children loved. All went quiet.

Mrs Warnes stood on the stage, welcomed everyone and said, "The children have worked very hard, and we hope you will enjoy our play, *The Road to Bethlehem*."

The audience clapped.

Then she said, "To open this evening we have Ellen Lankester, accompanied by Mr Eddie Gee, singing 'Little Donkey'."

Once again all was quiet.

Ellen came onstage and Mr Gee started to play the introduction. Then Ellen began to sing. It was beautiful.

When she had finished the audience clapped and clapped. Grandy had tears in his eyes. Ellen left the stage to hurry and change into her Herod costume while one of the boys came onstage to play a cornet solo. He played 'Jingle Bells'. Once again Mr Gee accompanied him, and he would be the pianist for all the music.

Once more the audience clapped.

Now it was time for the play to begin. It began with the children singing behind the curtains 'Once in Royal David's City'. The curtains opened and the shepherds were sitting round a fire watching their sheep. The Angel Gabriel appeared and the true Christmas story unfolded.

The audience were entranced.

When the play had finished and all the children were onstage, Mr Gee started playing the piano. Ellen stood and sang 'Mary's Boy Child', and the first performance finished as it had started.

The whole audience stood to applaud, and it seemed to go on forever. It would all be repeated three more times.

The year drew to a close and all was good.

CHAPTER 5

Ellen's life continued in much the same way. She had started secondary school, and at fourteen she was made a Senior Soldier of the Salvation Army (all Salvationists are known as soldiers).

On Saturday 4 March 1966 Ellen's world fell apart. Her beloved Grandy went to heaven from the West Norwich Hospital. He had pneumonia. Ellen's heart had been broken.

On Tuesday the 14th Murrell Cork Funeral Directors brought Grandy home to Bacton Road and placed his coffin in the front room. The curtains had been closed and everything was ready for Jack's friends to pay their respects. They came from the Oddfellows, the Forget-Me-Not Club, the friends he played dominoes with, and some people even came from the Salvation Army. At every opportunity Ellen would go into the front room to be with her adored Grandy. Jack's funeral service was to take place on the 16th at the Salvation Army Hall at 2.30 p.m.

On the morning of the funeral wreaths began to arrive at the little cottage. There were wreaths in the shape of a domino and a blue forget-me-not, and many others of various shapes and colours. Rene, Audrey, Kathleen and Wilfred's arrangement was of white roses. Ellen had used her own pocket money for a posy of lilies of the valley with one red rose – Grandy's favourite flowers. The family flowers would go on the coffin, and by the time the hearse came the floors of the two rooms in the cottage were covered in flowers. Another car had to be sent for. The family had decided that they would walk the short distance to the hall. When they got there it was full.

The service was lovely with Grandy's favourite songs, 'The Old Rugged Cross' and 'Trust and Obey'. Afterwards Jack was buried beside his wife, Nellie, in the cemetery in Bacton Road.

Then it was back to the cottage and life had to go on. Ellen wondered how she could carry on. After all, Grandy had been the one person who loved her unconditionally all her life. She was distraught, but no one seemed to understand and just told Ellen to pull herself together, saying she'd have to get used to it. Ellen tried so hard, but she wouldn't and couldn't get used to losing Grandy.

Two weeks later Ellen was told it was her turn to be the May queen for the Salvation Army anniversary event. It was the last thing she wanted. She felt physically sick, but there was nothing she could do about it. Salvation Army life was hard and the young people had little time for themselves. Ellen wasn't on her own and somehow it helped knowing others were in the same situation. It's true there were some fun times and the occasional friend's party to go to.

The anniversary event came and went, as did the summer holidays. Audrey and Ellen went to Butlin's in Skegness for two weeks and it did them good. It was a happy time that went by far too quickly.

Back home in Bacton Road life went by without incident. However, one Saturday the radio stopped working, and Audrey decided she would have a look at it. She thought the fuse had gone, so she took the back of the plug off, put a new fuse in, plugged it back in the wall and 'BANG!' Audrey's arm was black, but she just laughed and asked Ellen to go next door and fetch Uncle Stan.

He came round, saw Audrey and said, "Gal, Audrey, what are you a-doin' on? You'll blow yourself up."

She looked at him and said, "Well, I didn't," and they both laughed.

Stan fixed the radio and went back next door.

The next few months went by. The winter of 1966 was to be

one of the harshest winters known for many years, but life continued with people helping each other. Major Maurice Hayllett of the Salvation Army would walk to outlying villages to see the elderly folk of the corps, often taking milk and bread. He was truly a one-off.

1967 was the year Ellen would leave school. She had decided she wanted to train to be a children's nanny.

The last day of school arrived and there was great excitement among the friends. Some of them knew what they wanted to do; others had no idea. Many of them lived in North Walsham, so they would see each other in the town; the Salvation Army young people would see each other at the hall. At the end of the day there were some happy tears as school had finished, and some sad tears as friends said goodbye, realising it was time to grow up and go off into the world of work.

Ellen had two weeks' holiday with Auntie Kathleen in Streatham Vale. When she came home she would start her training, which would take three years.

Ellen loved the training and all that she was learning about childcare. She adored the children and longed to get her first job as a nanny.

Three years passed and Ellen qualified, then after about a month she got a position with a family in North Walsham, with two girls and a boy. Ellen ensured that the children were polite and well mannered, always saying please and thank you. They grew to love Ellen and enjoyed story time, and trips to the park and seaside. But, as we all know, children grow up far too quickly, and when the children started secondary school Ellen left the family. She had been with them four years.

In 1974 Ellen became a volunteer at the Air Training Corps at Manor Road School, and with her friend Jackie they ran the tuck shop on Tuesday and Thursday evenings. Ellen had also started working for another family in the town and she felt that her life was good. Oh yes, she still missed Grandy, though it had been eight years since his death. Ellen was still involved with the Salvation Army, but now and again she would have a Sunday off.

1975 was to be the year that would change Ellen's life forever. While running the tuck shop on a Tuesday evening in early March, a handsome young Royal Air Force policeman came to the ATC as an instructor. He said good evening to Jackie and Ellen. The following Thursday he came back, and this time Ellen was in the tuck shop on her own.

During the break he asked for a coffee and said, "Hello. I'm Keith."

Ellen also introduced herself, and at the end of the evening Keith offered to dry the dishes for Ellen, and when they had finished he kissed Ellen goodnight.

When Ellen got home she told Audrey she had met the man she was going to marry.

The next week Keith was at the ATC again on Tuesday and Thursday. He took Ellen home both evenings and asked if he could take Ellen out for a meal on Saturday. He said he would pick Ellen up at 10.30 a.m. and meet Audrey.

Ellen was ready when Keith arrived. Audrey liked him.

Keith said to Ellen, "I need to go into town to get a battery for my watch."

They went into Mears, the jeweller's.

Keith got down on one knee and said to Ellen, "Will you marry me?"

Ellen said, "Yes."

Everyone in the shop cheered.

Keith asked to see engagement rings, and a sapphire-and-diamond ring was chosen. They would be officially engaged the next day, Sunday 23 March, which was Easter Sunday. They then went back to Bacton Road to show Audrey the ring, and she loved it.

Later they went to see Rene and Wilfred. Rene immediately thought Keith was a lovely young man and was thrilled for her daughter. Wilfred's reception was a bit cooler.

Later in the evening Keith and Ellen had a lovely meal

together, and before returning to RAF Coltishall Ellen invited him to Sunday lunch at Audrey's and decided this would be an excellent opportunity to show Keith off to her Salvation Army friends. He said that he would be delighted to accept, and he would meet Ellen at Audrey's at 10 a.m. Ellen already knew that she loved him, and Keith told Audrey that he loved Ellen right from the start. Keith was thirty-one and Ellen was twenty-three.

On Sunday morning Keith met Ellen at Bacton Road and they walked to the hall together. Several of the corps folk were very surprised to see Ellen with a young man and even more surprised when they saw her engagement ring. However, they were very pleased for her. Keith and Ellen had another three wonderful days together, during which they booked the church in town for the wedding and the community centre was booked for the reception. The wedding was to take place on Saturday 1 May 1976.

At the beginning of April 1975 Keith was posted to RAF Troodos, in Cyprus, for a year. Keith and Ellen would therefore do all their courting by letter.

The day before Keith left he handed Wilfred £1,500 to start arrangements for the wedding, saying, "Whatever Ellen wants she can have."

You should have seen the look on Wilfred's face. I don't think he had ever held so much money. Rene promised Keith that they would carry out his wishes.

As you can imagine, the next few months were very busy with wedding preparations. As Keith had wished, Ellen had stopped work. As he was heard to tell Audrey, "There is no need for Ellen to work – she will want for nothing."

The first thing Audrey, Ellen and Rene did was to write a guest list. Keith had sent a list of his guests from Cyprus.

The next question Ellen asked Rene and Audrey was "Who do we ask, and who do we not?"

After several days the total number of guests was 163. The next thing to do was choose bridesmaids and ushers. Keith's best man would be his dearest friend, David, also an RAF policeman. Invitations were next on the list – these were ordered from Rounce & Wortley in Hall Lane, where Ellen's friend David worked. Ellen was going to have seven bridesmaids and three ushers – John Dyball, John Carr and Cyril Morse.

By now it was August 1975 and Ellen had a letter from Keith at least three or four times a week. Their love for each other was growing across the miles. Being apart was very hard for them both. Through the letters it was discussed as to what Keith would wear. Ellen asked if he could wear his RAF uniform, and he said he would ask for permission. Ellen sent Keith samples of material for the colours of the bridesmaids' dresses and photos of wedding cakes, so Keith could help choose even though he was so far away. Keith told Ellen in a letter at the beginning of October he had got the wedding rings, which he had designed. Ellen was becoming more and more excited by the day. The decision had been made that two bridesmaids would be in rose pink, two in lemon, two in turquoise and the smallest in cream with a turquoise sash. Their dresses would be made by Ellen and Rene, and Audrey said that she would help, but as she couldn't cut straight (she once altered a pair of Grandy's trousers and cut one leg six inches shorter than the other) Audrey said that she would pin and tack. The wedding cake would be a four-tier thruppenny-bit shape with bells, doves and horseshoes around each tier and a bride and groom on top. The Norfolk Nuts Band was booked for the dance after the reception.

In the middle of November Keith wrote to say that he had booked a ten-minute phone call to Ellen for Christmas Eve, so as Rene and Audrey didn't have a phone Ellen would go to a friend's.

During the first week in December Ellen, Audrey and Rene went into Norwich on the train to get the wedding dress. It was so exciting, yet a little bit scary. Ellen tried on a lot of dresses and finally one was chosen – white, of course. There was also a twenty-five-foot train and a lovely diamanté tiara. It cost £380 (a colossal amount of money in 1975). Ellen was so proud that she had paid in cash. When Ellen got home to Bacton Road the dress was hung on the picture rail in the back bedroom (Ellen's room). Every time Ellen went upstairs she would unzip the bag and look at the dress.

Audrey laughingly said, "You'll wear that dress away by keeping looking at it."

Ellen smiled and gave Audrey a hug.

Audrey knew in a few short months Ellen would be leaving Bacton Road and she would miss her terribly. Audrey now had a lovely man in her life – they adored each other.

Audrey's friend said, "Why don't you get married?"

Audrey replied, "Not until my Ellen is settled."

Ellen wanted her auntie to be happy too.

As Christmas week approached Ellen became so excited at the thought of the promised Christmas phone call. Ellen iced the Christmas cake, and began wrapping presents to put beneath the Christmas tree, which was already in the front room and decorated. The Nativity scene was on the sideboard as it had been every year since Audrey was a little girl.

On 23 December Audrey made thirty-six mince pies. Eric Lowe, the bandmaster at the Salvation Army, had told Audrey that as this was Ellen's last Christmas at home the band would be down on Christmas Eve at 11.30 p.m. to play carols outside. (The North Walsham Salvation Army Band used to play in the town, and then split into three bands of ten and played around all the little villages every Christmas.)

Christmas Eve arrived and at seven forty-five Ellen walked up to her friend's for the 8-p.m. phone call, and at exactly 8 p.m. the phone rang and it was Keith. It was strange as they had to wait a few seconds to hear each other. The call was over far too quickly, and what was said that evening between those two young people so very much in love will never be told.

As Ellen began to walk back home it began to snow. It was magical. When Ellen got to the top of Bacton Road she could hear the band playing in the distance and she wished they were nearer, not knowing they would be down to the small cottage later.

Ellen went indoors and Audrey made a hot chocolate. As she had just taken some sausage rolls out of the oven they had one each. Audrey's new man, John, was there, so the three of them sat and chatted for quite some time.

Then Audrey said, smiling, "Listen! Can you hear it?"

Ellen said, "Oh, Audy, it's the band. Let's go and listen."

They opened the front door and Eric asked Ellen what she would like them to play. She asked for 'Silent Night' – Grandy's favourite. As the band played, tears rolled down Ellen's cheeks. They also played 'Softly the Night Is Sleeping' and 'Away in a Manger'. Afterwards the sixteen bandsmen and women came into Audrey's warm, loving little cottage and ate hot mince pies and drank home-made ginger wine by a roaring fire.

Soon it was time for them to leave with happy Christmas wishes ringing in their ears. As 1975 drew to a close Ellen thought to herself, 'In five months' time I'll be married and in a home with my darling Keith.'

CHAPTER 6

The New Year began with more wedding preparations. The meal for the reception would be roast beef or chicken with roast or new potatoes, cauliflower, peas, green beans, carrots, Yorkshire pudding and gravy; the dessert would be sherry trifle or apple pie with custard or cream. Champagne had been ordered for the toast, and for those who didn't drink there would be fruit juice. The next thing on the list was flowers and buttonholes. Ellen would carry red and gold roses, gold freesias and lilies of the valley – all flowers that Grandy loved. The bridesmaids would carry pink and lemon carnations, and the smallest bridesmaid, who was three years old, would carry a little basket of freesias and lilies of the valley. Audrey, Rene and Kathleen would have freesia buttonholes; the men would have white carnations. A friend of Rene's was in charge of the church Flower Guild and she had seen Ellen grow up with her daughter. She told Rene she would do the flowers in church as a gift to Ellen. They would be arrangements of spring flowers. Rene was so thrilled with her kindness.

At the beginning of March invitations were sent out, and two weeks later replies were coming in thick and fast. Audrey, Rene and Ellen ventured into Norwich to buy Audrey and Rene's outfits for the wedding. Audrey's favourite colour was pink and Rene's was green. After looking in several shops both sisters found a dress and jacket, but Audrey's was pale green with tiny little pink and white flowers on it; Rene's was rose pink edged with navy. Audrey bought a white hat and Rene a navy one. After stopping for coffee they went to Burton's, the tailor's, to pick up Wilfred's suit. Rene

45

bought him a new shirt. All in all it had been a very happy day.

On Sunday morning before the 11 a.m. meeting Ellen handed out the invitations to some of the Salvation Army folk. It was quite funny watching them open the envelopes and looking at each other, signalling 'Have you got one?' just as the service was about to start.

By the end of March all the replies were in and the final total was for 152 to sit down for the reception, plus another sixty for the evening dance and buffet.

On the evening of 26 April Ellen didn't know what to do with herself. Her Keith was coming home the next day. He would be on the 1-p.m. train into Norwich and Ellen would go to meet him. Ellen tried to keep busy, but all she could think about was seeing her Keith and the wedding.

After trying to sleep without having much success, Ellen got up at 6 a.m., went downstairs, made a cup of coffee and a slice of toast and sat in the front room thinking about what the future would hold. Ellen was deep in thought when Audrey came into the room.

"Are you all right, darling?" she asked.

Ellen said, "I'm fine – very excited and a little bit scared."

Audrey went over to her niece and gave her a hug and said, "Don't you ever forget how much I love you. No matter where you are in the world I will always be here for you."

They both began to cry.

Audrey said, "Come on – we're silly old fools. Let's get washed and dressed – there are still things to do."

A short while later Rene came into the cottage with an envelope for Ellen. Apparently it had been left at the shop with Wilfred. The writing on the envelope wasn't very good. It said in capital letters, 'MISS ELLEN LANKESTER, Please accept the enclosed from someone who has always loved you. Be happy, darling.'

Audrey and Rene both looked at each other then said together, "Open it."

Ellen stared at it for a moment then gave it to Audrey and said, "I can't – you open it."

When Audrey opened it the three of them looked at each other in absolute disbelief. It contained £750 in £10 and £20 notes.

Ellen threw it on the settee, saying, "I can't have all that money. I don't know who it's from, do you?"

"No," they said.

Rene said, "It's obviously someone who knows and loves you, to have left it with your dad."

"Yes, but who?" Ellen said.

"Come with me and we will go to the shop and see what Dad knows."

Wilfred told them that a lady he didn't know had taken it into the shop and just said, "Mr Lankester, please give this to Ellen."

Audrey, Rene and Wilfred said that Ellen should accept the money in the way it had been given – with love. Ellen listened to what they said and decided that she would put the money in the bank. Ellen never knew where or from whom the money came.

Audrey and Rene were going to stay in town and do some shopping; Keith was going to stay with Rene and Wilfred till the wedding.

Ellen said goodbye to Rene and Audrey went home to Bacton Road to change and have a few quiet moments before she got the train to meet her Keith. They had been apart over a year and she was so excited.

On arrival at Norwich, Ellen had ten minutes to wait. It seemed like an hour. Then at last the 1-p.m. train was there, and she saw Keith. They stood on the platform in a loving embrace, oblivious to all around. They walked hand in hand to platform four to wait for the train back to North Walsham, where Rene and Audrey were waiting at Morris Road.

As Keith and Ellen sat on the train they had so much to tell each other, but for a moment or two they sat hand in hand in silence.

When they arrived in North Walsham it was just a short walk to Morris Road. As they got to the gate the front door was open and Rene had 'Welcome Home' by Peters and Lee playing on the record player. Audrey and Rene were so happy to see Keith again.

When everyone was settled Rene made a pot of tea. She had also made some scones and sausage rolls. Audrey had made a sponge cake. They sat down together to catch up. There would be a family meal later when Wilfred got back from the shop.

After tea Keith said, "I'm rather tired. Would anyone mind if I went for a lie-down for a while?"

Of course no one minded.

Rene said, "The poor boy must be worn out."

After a couple of hours Keith came downstairs with some packages. He had brought Audrey and Rene beautiful Cypriot leather handbags. There was one for Kathleen too – she would be home on Thursday. There were also silk scarfs for the ladies, and for Wilfred and John a leather wallet. Keith had brought six stunning silver bracelets for the older bridesmaids, and for the little one a dog that walked, sat up and barked.

For Ellen there was a handbag, a gold watch, a necklace and a beautiful silk shawl embroidered with birds and flowers in every colour you could imagine. Keith also gave Ellen a beautiful solid-silver tea service. Needless to say, everyone was thrilled with their gifts, and thought the bridesmaids' bracelets were exquisite.

Rene went to put the veg on for dinner. Wilfred would be home at 6 p.m. They were going to have roast chicken with all the trimmings. Wilfred no longer complained that Ellen still didn't eat meat; she had taken a liking to chicken. For pudding Rene had made a steamed syrup suet pudding. The table was set and at six fifteen the six of them sat down and had a lovely meal together. John had joined them. Wilfred and John were very pleased with their gifts.

After dinner, when everyone had sat down, Keith said, "I have something to tell you and show you."

First Keith took two small boxes from his pocket. They contained the two gold wedding rings that he had designed and had made in Cyprus. They were gorgeous, with a pattern of flowers.

Ellen wanted to try hers on, but Keith said, "No, you get to put it on on Saturday and then never take it off." He then said that after Ellen and he were married he would have a month's holiday, then Ellen would be joining him in Cyprus. It had been expected, and now the family knew it would be a reality and that Ellen would be thousands of miles away.

Ellen asked, "How long till I come to Cyprus? What do I need to bring? What can't I bring? Will I need vaccinations? If so, where will I have to go?"

Keith said, "Slow down – we'll talk about it soon."

The rest of the evening went very well.

At 10 p.m. Keith looked very tired, so Ellen said, "Goodnight. I'll see you at Audrey's in the morning."

Audrey and Ellen got into John's car for the short drive back to Bacton Road. It had been a long but happy day.

The next morning Keith came down to Audrey's. Ellen told him she had booked a week in a guest house in Great Yarmouth for after the wedding. Then Ellen and Keith would go to the Isle of Wight for a week and stay with Keith's mum and dad, and meet various aunts and uncles. When Keith and Ellen got engaged Ellen was thrilled to discover that she would have a sister and two brothers after the wedding: Keith's lovely sister, Dawn, and wonderful brothers, Kevin and Julian.

Later that morning Ellen's Uncle Billy came into town. He stopped at Audrey's for a coffee. He was very fond of Ellen. He lived in the village of Trunch, about three miles from North Walsham. Billy was Wilfred's older brother, but they hadn't spoken to each other for years. However, Billy was coming to the wedding. He also spoke such very broad Norfolk that Keith had to ask several times, "What did Billy say?" During the conversation Keith said that he was going to hire a car on Friday to go to Norwich and pick up the wedding cake.

Uncle Billy said, "You dun't ha' ter do that, my booty. You can borra my car for as long as ya like – there's no hurra."

Keith said, "Ellen, would you translate that into English, please?"

Ellen said, "He said that you can borrow his car for as long as you need it – there is no hurry."

This was astonishing as Uncle Billy had NEVER let anyone borrow anything before.

Audrey, Keith and Ellen went into town to do some last-minute bits. Audrey said that she would see them later for lunch. Ellen and Keith went down to Freddie Hall's florist to take the ribbon for the bouquets. Ellen then went to Fullers to get some tights.

Two more days and she would be Mrs Christian. Ellen was so excited. One more day and she would meet Keith's mum and dad. When they arrived they would stay with Rene and Wilfred. Keith would stay with family friends to sleep. Other guests would be arriving and several rooms had been booked at the Beechwood Hotel and other guest houses in the town. Almost everything was ready.

On Friday morning Ellen and Keith went to fetch the cake. It was beautiful. They took it straight to the community centre, where the staff were setting the tables ready for the reception. There were a few changes to be made to the seating plan. The tables looked lovely, and all that was needed were the flowers – pink and white roses – which would arrive in the morning.

Ellen and Keith then went into town and went into the church. The sight that met their eyes was stunning. There were daffodils in every hue of yellow, cream and white, and tulips in pink, white and yellow. Keith and Ellen were quite overwhelmed by it all. It had been such a wonderful gesture from the Flower Guild.

While in the church, Keith said, "Oh my goodness, the aisle is long." (It is the second longest in Norfolk.)

They just sat there taking it all in.

Later that evening there would be a full wedding rehearsal. Keith and Ellen went into town and met some of Ellen's friends and Keith was introduced. Keith then went into Marjoram's for a shirt and tie.

When they got back to Audrey's, Rene was there for lunch. Just as they sat down Kathleen arrived, so they all had cottage pie and veg together.

After lunch everyone sat down for a good old natter.

Kathleen and Keith got on like a house on fire. When Keith asked Kathleen if she would bless the wedding rings she was thrilled. Around 6.30 p.m. everyone met at the church for the rehearsal. Wilfred and the bridesmaids were waiting. Keith was right: the aisle was long – very long, in fact. Everything went well. It had been a wonderfully happy, busy day.

Keith took the car back to Uncle Billy, and he brought Keith back to Audrey's. Ellen had got changed, ready for everyone to go up to Rene and Wilfred's for a large family buffet and to meet Keith's mum and dad. Ellen and Keith went up to Rene's with Audrey in John's car.

Just as they got indoors Ida and Eric, Keith's mum and dad, arrived and all went indoors for introductions. The next to arrive was Keith's best man, David. Keith went outside to meet him. As Ellen was looking out of the window a strange but very pretty lady ran straight up to Keith, threw her arms round his neck and kissed him. Ellen shot outside to see who this woman was. It turned out to be one of Keith's dearest friends, Pam, with her husband, John. Pam later became one of Ellen's closest and dearest friends. More and more people were arriving by the minute, and the house was in a state of wonderfully happy chaos. Ellen took Ida upstairs to show her the wedding dress. She loved it.

At the end of the evening when everyone said goodnight they knew tomorrow was going to be a wonderful, long, busy day.

CHAPTER 7

On 1 May 1976, the wedding day, at 7 a.m. Ellen got out of bed and could smell bacon. She went downstairs, where Audrey had set the table with the best china and had bacon sandwiches ready for breakfast.

At 9 a.m. Ellen walked up to the hairdresser's, where she met Rene and three of the older bridesmaids. When all their hair had been done the bridesmaids went home to fetch their dresses. They would meet up at Rene's later to get changed as Ellen was going to leave from Morris Road. Rene and Ellen then went over to the community centre to make sure everything was ready. The flowers had arrived and the tables looked lovely. Rene and Ellen then went back to Morris Road. Ellen set out everything needed for herself and the bridesmaids to change in Rene and Wilfred's bedroom. Ellen sat on the bed thinking about the next few hours, wishing that her beloved Grandy could have been there, but somehow she knew he was watching.

As she was deep in thought the doorbell rang – the flowers had arrived and Ellen couldn't believe how stunning they were. The perfume filled the front room. Freddie Hall, the florist, said that he would take whichever buttonholes were needed down to Audrey's.

The postman arrived in a van, which was very unusual for North Walsham. He had so many packages which contained presents, and lots of cards full of good wishes for the bride and groom.

The wedding was set for 2.30 p.m., so Rene had done

sandwiches for lunch for everyone. Ellen couldn't eat she was so excited and nervous.

Around 1.30 p.m. the bridesmaids arrived to get ready, then Joy, the chief bridesmaid, helped Ellen to get ready. Audrey and Kathleen came to see Ellen before she left for the church. They both cried, as did Rene and Ida. Even Eric and Wilfred had a tear in their eyes. Kathleen would later drive Keith to church in her car from Audrey's – it already had the white wedding ribbon on it. Ellen was looking out of the front-room window when a white Rolls-Royce went past.

Ellen said, "Wow! Someone's got a Rolls for their wedding. Aren't they lucky?" as it disappeared round the corner, only for it to turn round and stop right outside the house.

Rene said, "That's for you, darling."

Ellen couldn't believe it.

Rene, Ida and Eric were the first to go, with the three smallest bridesmaids. It would then come back for the other four. Once all the bridesmaids had gone, the car would come back for Ellen and Wilfred. It was 2.25 p.m. Ellen was going to be five minutes late, as is traditional.

The drive through town was lovely. Ellen felt like the Queen and waved to people. When they arrived at the church she could not believe her eyes – there were people everywhere, including many of Wilfred's customers, Ellen's old school friends, and a lot of people from the Salvation Army. Some of the Salvation Army folk were guests and already in the church. As Ellen approached the church she was met with a wall of cameras. The official photographer was waiting with the bridesmaids and Canon David Maurice, who would lead the service. Inside the church porch many of the ATC cadets had lined up to meet Ellen and Wilfred before they went into the church. More photos were taken, then it was time.

Ellen and Wilfred stepped inside the church door. She noticed Keith's RAF cap, so she knew he was there. As Mr Eddie Gee started playing 'Here Comes the Bride' they were off down the aisle slowly. Ellen wanted to take everything in of this wonderful day. Everyone had turned round to face Ellen and Wilfred. The church was absolutely packed.

Everyone was smiling, and Ellen thought, 'I will never forget this day as long as I live.'

Then she was by Keith's side. Oh, he looked so handsome in his RAF police uniform.

The service started, then David Maurice began. He asked, "Who gives this woman to this man?" and Wilfred said, "I do."

Keith and Ellen exchanged their vows and exchanged rings.

All at once David said, "I now pronounce you husband and wife. You may kiss your bride."

Mr Gee played 'The Wedding March' and the bridal party went to sign the register. They then went out through the doors to another wall of cameras, and confetti being thrown. Ellen was given two horseshoes, a silver bell and a number plate, U2 R1. Many more photos were taken and congratulations were given, then it was up to the reception.

As is usual, the bridal party lined up to shake hands or kiss everyone as they came in. Keith's friend had come from Cyprus with his wife and daughter. The reception was lovely; the meal was delicious. There were the usual speeches, but no one was rude. The best man read out seven telegrams, and in among them was a cheque for £365. At 7 p.m. the band started playing as Keith and Ellen had their first dance to 'Stranger on the Shore'. The rest of the celebrations were wonderful.

At 11 p.m. the bride and groom were driven away to start their honeymoon in Great Yarmouth. Keith and Ellen would discover later that someone had got into Rene and Wilfred's during the reception and slashed the pillows on Rene's bed so that when Ida and Eric went to bed feathers went everywhere. They thought Keith and Ellen were staying in Morris Road overnight – oops! It was a good thing Rene saw the funny side of it. However, the same people – we know who you are, he he! – also wrapped toilet roll around all the roses in the front garden. Wilfred was not so amused. Ida and Eric would stay with Rene and Wilfred for a week.

Meanwhile Keith and Ellen were enjoying time together in Great Yarmouth. Later they would go down to the Isle of Wight.

During the week in Yarmouth Keith and Ellen rang home. There was a message for Keith to ask if he would like married quarters in the village of Pano Platres; he would need to send a telegram if he wished to accept, which he did. However, the quarters wouldn't be ready, so Keith would fly back to Cyprus on 5 June alone.

Keith tried to comfort Ellen, saying, "I have to go, darling. It won't be long before you come out to join me. Be strong."

How could she be strong? She was about to lose the man she loved more than anything in the world, and no one could tell her how long it would be before they were together again. It was horrible.

Keith said to Audrey, "Look after my Ellen and keep her safe."

Audrey said, "You know I will."

Keith flew out to Cyprus on 5 June, and Ellen would have to wait till 8 July before she would fly out to join him.

On the morning of 7 July Audrey, Rene and Ellen caught the train to Norwich to catch the train to London. From there they would catch another train to Swindon, where they were picked up by an RAF coach and taken to RAF Brize Norton. On arrival, Ellen checked in and her suitcases were taken. She just had an overnight bag and handbag. Later Audrey, Rene and Ellen were provided with a lovely meal and then Audrey and Rene, who were allowed to stay overnight at Brize Norton, were shown their room. Ellen was in the room next door.

Apparently, Rene kept Audrey up most of the night saying, "Oh look, Audrey, there's another aeroplane." Rene was aeroplane crazy.

The following morning after breakfast Audrey and Rene were allowed to accompany Ellen to the departure lounge. When Ellen's name was called the three of them said a very tearful goodbye.

The next thing Ellen knew she was on the plane flying out to her Keith. Ellen had never been on a plane and she loved every minute of it.

Keith met her off the plane at RAF Akrotiri and Keith drove

them up the mountain to Pano Platres, where the married quarters were. It was a lovely two-bedroom flat set in a horseshoe of pine trees. There was a huge grapevine on the patio, with cherry, orange and lemon trees all around it. Keith didn't have to go to work until Monday, so he was going to show Ellen round the village and some of the island. After doing some shopping they both went home. Keith had prepared a meal earlier, so they were soon sitting down to eat. At last they were together.

Over the next few weeks and months Ellen learnt a few Cypriot words. She often walked down the mountain into the village. It was very pretty and people were friendly. Ellen had joined the wives' club and made some new friends.

Early in December 1976 Ellen and Keith found out they were to have a baby. They were so thrilled, and by now Rene had a phone, so Keith booked a phone call for Christmas Eve. Ellen had written to Rene so that Audrey and John could be there too. At 7 p.m. UK time the phone rang at Morris Road.

Rene said, "Hello."

Ellen said, "Hello, Grandma."

Rene said, "What did you say?"

When Ellen said 'Grandma' again, Rene called Audrey to the phone and they both cried tears of utter joy.

Rene said, "Oh, when?"

Keith said, "Around the 10th of August."

Rene said, "I'll get some wool and Audrey and I will start knitting."

Ellen said, "Slow down – there's plenty of time."

After wishing each other a happy Christmas it was time to say their goodbyes. Other families were waiting to call their loved ones, and they were only allotted ten minutes for each call.

That first Christmas Eve together Keith and Ellen went to a beautiful little church for midnight Mass. It was enchanting. It was in the diocese of Jerusalem. They went home happy and content.

When they awoke on Christmas morning and opened the curtains there was four feet of snow on the patio. The mountain and pine trees looked so pretty, but my goodness it was cold. The heating was turned up and a cup of coffee was made. Breakfast of bacon, eggs and toast was soon ready.

After breakfast it was time to open the gifts that had been sent from the UK. Audrey had made a lovely deep-blue jumper for Keith and a pink cardigan for Ellen. Rene had sent slippers and pyjamas along with ladies' hankies from Kathleen. There were scarves and gloves (very handy). Ellen had bought Keith a gold watch and he had given Ellen a beautiful silver bracelet and a Kenwood Chef with all the attachments. It turned out to be a wonderful first Christmas.

The snow continued into the New Year and Keith took Ellen up to Troodos village to watch the skiing. By the end of February it was still snowing up the mountain and the temperature had been minus twenty-five for over a month, but down at Ladies' Mile in Akrotiri it was so warm on the beach they were able to swim in the sea and have a picnic.

Ellen was used to Keith going off to work at RAF Troodos in the mornings. She would go for a walk or pop into the village. The Cypriot people always had time for the service families. Life was wonderful.

Two sisters ran a shop in Pano Platres village that sold craft items – wool, tapestries, needlepoint equipment and such. Ellen bought a needlepoint picture and the embroidery silks. In the UK silks were fifty-five pence each; in Cyprus they were five pence each. Another thing that was an amazing price was leather goods. Keith and Ellen had real-leather coats made for £60 for the two. Table linen was exquisite. Ladies could often be seen making lace by the roadside. There were fruit trees everywhere. Thirty peaches would cost twenty pence, as would oranges. Cherries were sold by the bucketful. The fruit, veg and meat markets were a sight to behold. There were certainly no hygiene restrictions as meat, fruit and veg all lay on tables together.

As winter turned to spring and spring to summer the island

came alive with tourists, yet somehow the villages still kept their charm.

By June Ellen was seven months pregnant. Audrey and Rene had sent little knitted coats from the UK. Everything was ready.

On 8 August 1977 baby Victoria Alicia was born, weighing five pounds six ounces. She had dark-brown hair and like all new babies had dark-blue eyes. Keith and Ellen thought she was the most beautiful baby in the world.

After four days Mum and baby came home. Baby Victoria settled into a routine. She was a very happy baby and rarely cried. Ellen wished Audrey and Rene could see her, but Audrey was terrified of flying and Rene was far from well. Photos were taken and sent back to the UK. Keith and Ellen thought that their lives had been blessed.

As the months went by, Victoria started to grow into a sweet little girl. Her eyes had turned brown, just like Rene's. Christmas came around once more and Keith and Ellen had managed to get a Christmas tree. They decorated it and put it in the front window, which looked out down the road. Keith and Ellen couldn't understand why the villagers kept coming up the road and pointing at the front window, until one day they were told the villagers had never seen a decorated Christmas tree. It fascinated them (Cypriots celebrate Easter more than Christmas).

On Christmas Eve the snow started to fall once more and it continued for weeks.

On the evening of 6 February Ellen tucked Victoria into her cot at 7 p.m. as usual, but when Keith and Ellen went in to check on her at 10.30 p.m., as they went to bed, they found baby Victoria had gone to heaven. It was a cot death. Their world had been turned upside down and their hearts broken.

The RAF doctor came very quickly. He was a lovely man – the families called him Uncle Ted. A week later Victoria was buried.

The next few months went by in a blur. Why? How could this happen? Keith and Ellen's love got them through this sad time. Somehow it seemed to grow stronger. They loved each other so very much. Life continued much the same as before, with Keith working in the mornings, and afternoons spent together.

One afternoon while in the village Keith stopped to talk to the chief of police, Sergeant Takis Kypriano. The RAF and local police worked closely together. Takis told Keith there was to be an evening dinner at the police station in two weeks' time, and they would be delighted if Keith and Ellen would attend. Keith said that they would love to.

Takis also said, "Would you wear your best uniform and could Ellen wear a long evening gown?"

It was very fortunate that a dressmaker in the village could make a dress in three days. Ellen already had several day dresses made by her, so the next stop was Andrula's. Ellen chose a deep-blue material with little gold rosebuds on it. She also chose another in deep pink. They would be ready in the week. It was just the tonic Keith and Ellen needed.

Keith was the only RAF policeman who lived in the village, and because of this he had become very well liked by the villagers, shopkeepers and hoteliers. He was very well respected for his fair no-nonsense approach. Ellen was so very proud of him.

Ellen loved her life in the village of Pano Platres. It was no good going shopping if she was in a hurry. She would go into Olga and Tommis' little gift shop, where they would insist she should sit down and have a glass of Coke, then on to the grocery shop and a coffee, where she handed her list over to Andy, who would deliver her shopping later. If Paul from the hotel spotted her, he would expect her to go in and enjoy yet more hospitality, but of course there is only so much liquid anyone can drink when they have a long uphill walk home.

A week later Ellen collected the dresses she'd had made. They were lovely.

The evening of the dinner arrived. Keith looked very handsome in his best uniform complete with medal. His shoes shone so much you could see your face in them. Ellen wore the blue-and-gold dress with a gold necklace. They made a very smart couple.

Takis was sending a car to pick them up at 7.30 p.m.

Ellen said, "I wonder what the other ladies will wear."

Obviously Keith didn't know.

At seven twenty-five the car arrived and off they went for the evening. When they got to the police station Takis was waiting to greet them. He too was in his best uniform. He ushered them into a large room behind the police station, where twenty of Takis's policemen were waiting, all dressed in their best uniforms. Ellen wished she had brought a camera. The large table was set with crisp white linen – twenty-three place settings with the finest glassware and china, and at the centre of the table pale-pink roses. Ellen wondered where the other ladies were, and felt a bit self-conscious.

Takis said, "Officers, please meet Mrs Christian."

They all said, "*Calla speera, mam.*" (Good evening, ma'am.)
Ellen smiled.

Takis then said, "Shall we sit?"

Ellen didn't know what to do as twenty policemen each pulled out a chair for her.

When Takis said, "Come sit next to me," oh she was relieved.

Once seated, the meal began. White wine or fruit juice was poured into the glasses. There were stuffed vine leaves to start. They were delicious, as were the next three courses, beginning with lamb with new potatoes and stuffed tomatoes, then chicken and salad with Cyprus bread. I can tell you this is the most delicious bread you could ever eat. This was followed by strawberries, melon, peaches, raspberries and plums, then cheese and biscuits, and coffee.

Once coffee had been served, Takis stood and said, "Keith and Ellen, we have asked you here this evening to say thank you to Keith for all the help you have given to my officers whilst you have been in Pano Platres. It is greatly appreciated. A good working partnership is essential in the work we do."

The officers clapped. Ellen had a tear in her eyes.

Keith replied, saying that it was through hard work that the two police sections worked so well together, and long might it continue.

One of the youngest officers presented Ellen with a bouquet of roses in all shades of pink and cream. The evening came to a close at 11.20 p.m. and the car came to take Keith and Ellen home. It had been a wonderful evening.

In late September of 1977 Auntie Kathleen came to stay for two weeks. As Keith and Ellen now had a car, they picked her up from Larnaca Airport and drove back to Pano Platres. Kathleen loved it all.

One morning while Keith was at work and Kathleen and Ellen were sitting on the patio a huge iguana came walking across in front of them. Ellen had got used to them and they would eat out of Ellen's hand.

Kathleen was frightened, but Ellen said, "Sit still – he won't hurt you."

She gave him some grapes and when he had finished he calmly walked away.

Kathleen said, "I thought he was going to eat me."

Ellen just laughed.

When Keith finished work Ellen had packed a picnic so they could go to the beach. Kathleen couldn't believe how blue the sea was. She soon had her swimsuit on, and they all had a lovely afternoon together, then drove home tired but happy.

Kathleen loved the little churches dotted around the island. While she was there she saw a Cypriot wedding – much different to ours in the UK. Keith and Ellen had been very privileged to go to two weddings in Cyprus. These are held over three days. First there is a huge party for the whole village to attend, and this lasts well into the night, usually being on a Friday. On the Saturday the civil ceremony is followed by another all-night party. On the Sunday it is the church wedding, where the bride and groom make their vows. It is quite normal for 300 or 400 people to be at the three days of celebration. Many of them stay for the whole time, sleeping wherever they can find a space. The food just keeps on coming. It's not unusual to have twenty courses at each sitting. Cypriot couples are not given gifts; instead banknotes and cheques are pinned on the bride's dress and the groom's suit, sometimes running into many thousands of pounds.

Auntie Kathleen's holiday came to an end far too soon, and she was on her way back to the UK, taking all the love her heart could hold with her.

The rest of the year went by well enough, but Ellen had been told by the Doctor that she must never try for another baby – it would kill her. Keith and Ellen were sad, but accepted it, saying, "One day we will know why."

Christmas approached once more and they went to the little church on Christmas Eve. There were more of the service families this time. It was lovely. As before, the tree was in the front window. A few Christmas trees had appeared in houses in the village. The children loved them.

At the end of December Keith heard that he was to be posted back to the UK in the New Year.

CHAPTER 8

In 1978 Keith's posting came through. He would be going to RAF Wittering, near Peterborough, in April. There was so much to do – boxes to be packed, last-minute gifts to buy and saying goodbye to Victoria. A friend promised that there would always be flowers on her tiny grave.

On 27 April Keith and Ellen left Cyprus with heavy hearts. It was a beautifully warm, sunny day. However, when they arrived in the UK it was bitterly cold and snowing heavily. What a welcome back! They moved into two-bedroom married quarters on the camp, which were modestly furnished with furniture the RAF provided. All the quarters were furnished in the same way: all had magnolia paintwork in the lounge diner, the kitchen was blue, one bedroom was lemon and one was pale green. Keith and Ellen's deep sea boxes had been delivered, so once the heating had been put on and a cup of tea made they set to with the unpacking. First they made the beds, and while Ellen continued to unpack Keith went to find the NAAFI shop and do some food shopping. He was soon back and surprised and delighted to see that Ellen had put a cloth on the dining table and one or two of their ornaments and photos were put on the unit in the corner. Ellen said that they would soon make this place look like home with cushions and a throw over the sofa. You certainly couldn't say RAF quarters were pleasant; in fact they were anything but.

Once a few more bits had been unpacked, they sat down to a meal. After the washing-up was done they both had a bath and went to bed absolutely shattered, wondering what life had in store for them both. After being in Cyprus in a very friendly village and situation, this was so different. It didn't feel at all friendly.

Keith was at work all day, and sometimes when there was an exercise Keith didn't come home for days on end. No contact was allowed. Ellen began to hate service life.

In June Keith and Ellen had a two-week holiday and went back to North Walsham. They had hired a car and so set off early in the morning. As they got on to the A1 they heard the siren go off for an exercise, but they just kept going. Nothing was going to spoil their holiday.

Audrey and her new husband, John, Rene and Wilfred were all waiting at Audrey's to meet them. Oh my goodness, there were lots of tears! Ellen noticed a big change in Rene – she had been diagnosed with arthritis in both her knees and in her spine and was in a lot of pain. Audrey had laid on a lovely meal – one of Keith's favourites: home-made beef patty, mashed potatoes, mixed veg and gravy, followed by rhubarb crumble and custard. Audrey and John seemed very happy. He was a master carpenter and much younger than Audrey, but he treated her like the purest gold. They had a golden Labrador puppy called Sally, and she had taken an instant dislike to Ellen, just about tolerating Keith, much to everyone's amusement.

The next two weeks were absolute bliss – meeting up with friends, going to Yarmouth, Sheringham and Cromer, and on a Thursday going into town to the market.

The holiday was soon over and it was time to go back to Wittering. While Keith and Ellen had been away a new wives' club had begun, so Ellen thought she would join. There were flower-arranging demonstrations and a visit to a glass factory and a pottery where some of the wives tried making a bowl, but suddenly the club closed due to lack of interest.

The camp exercises became more regular.

One evening Keith had arranged a dinner at the RAOB club, where Keith was a member. Twenty guests were coming by coach from Keith's Mother Lodge in Melton Mowbray. Keith was so excited. The dinner was booked for 7.30 p.m., and

Keith was ready, dressed in his dinner suit, at 7.10 p.m. When the coach pulled up outside the house all hell broke loose – the siren went off for another f------ exercise to begin. There was nothing Keith could do but get changed and go to work. He was devastated. He had to leave his guests to get back on the coach and return the forty miles to Melton Mowbray. Thankfully many of them were either in the forces or ex-servicemen, but it was another evening ruined.

When Keith came home from the exercise three days later he said, "Enough is enough – I'm going to put my papers in and come out of the RAF. It's a wonderful life for a single man, but not for a married one."

At the beginning of November Keith heard that his request to leave the RAF had been accepted. He would leave eighteen months later, in April 1980. It was a relief.

As 1980 arrived Keith began looking for work. He applied for no end of jobs and went for numerous interviews, but to no avail. The recession of the early 1980s was starting to bite. Many said that he was overqualified.

Then at the end of February 1980 Keith found a job advertised that he really liked the look of – a property manager at a block of flats on Haverstock Hill in London. Keith made enquiries and was asked to attend an interview, so he travelled to London. When Keith came home that evening he told Ellen it was a lovely place and they would be given a one-bedroom flat on the ground floor. They would be allowed to furnish it as they wished, but it would be completely redecorated and new carpets would be put down. A washing machine, cooker and new fridge would be provided. Keith would have to wait about ten days to know if he was successful. Oh, how he had prayed that if it was God's will he would get the job!

A week later, as Keith and Ellen were having lunch, the phone rang.

Keith answered and a voice said, "Congratulations, Mr Christian. The job is yours and you can move into the flat anytime after 3 p.m. on the 3rd of March. By the way, would lemon be OK for the bedroom and pale peach for the lounge?"

Keith said, "Thank you so much. That's wonderful news."

The voice on the other end of the phone line said, "My pleasure, Mr Christian."

Keith and Ellen hugged each other, and Ellen cried, and a new stage in their lives was about to begin. Keith phoned Rene to give her the good news. She was delighted and said she would tell Audrey.

Keith and Ellen knew of a lovely warehouse that sold immaculate second-hand furniture, and decided the following morning they would go and see what they could find. Keith was now on leave, so they could take their time. They went to bed that night very happy.

The next morning after breakfast they set off for the warehouse. It was huge and spotlessly clean, and there was everything they could wish for at very reasonable prices.

After a good look round Keith said, "Have you seen a three-piece suite you like?"

Ellen said, "Yes, have you?"

Keith said, "You go to the one you like, and I'll go to the one I like."

Off they both went and they both stopped at the same one. It was deep-cream and peach. It was immaculate, and only £25. The next thing was a bed, preferably with a head and foot. A lovely oak one was chosen for £15. Keith and Ellen would buy a new mattress, a wardrobe, two bedside cabinets and a chest of drawers next, all for £30. Two rugs were also chosen along with four cushions, a dinner service, a small drop-leaf table and four dining chairs.

When they asked the man how much the rest of the purchases would be, he thought for a moment then said, "Give me £80 for everything and I'll be happy. Is that OK with you?"

Ellen and Keith didn't know what to say except "Thank you very much." They asked if the man would keep their purchases till Keith could hire a van to pick them up.

He said, "Where are you moving to and when?" Keith told him, and he said, "I go to London once a month, so for £10 I can deliver everything to you the day after you move. Is that OK?"

Keith said, "That's more than OK. Thank you."

Keith and Ellen walked home hand in hand and very happy. A few days later a new double mattress and pillows were ordered from John Lewis in Peterborough. As they had a store in London's Oxford Street they would deliver from there. Everything was working out fine.

Keith and Ellen were now busy packing and cleaning. When anyone left married quarters a housing officer would come round, put on white cotton gloves and go round every surface looking for dust, then any marks on the carpets, then put on another pair of white gloves and wipe his hands inside the oven. He then checked all the work surfaces, the sink and inside the cupboards in the kitchen. He'd go upstairs to the bathroom and bedrooms, even looking in the airing cupboard and wardrobes. If an indentation was found on the carpet from furniture you would be charged for it. He even took light bulbs out of their fittings to see if they were clean. Believe me, Ellen was a very placid person, but he certainly tried her patience, as he did that of many of the other wives. This performance was called 'marching out'.

The day before moving into their new flat Keith and Ellen travelled by train to London, where they would stay at the Victory Services Club in Seymour Street, near Marble Arch, overnight.

The next morning they were up bright and early for breakfast and they thought they would have a wander down Oxford Street, returning back to the club for lunch. At two thirty they got on the Tube and went to Stanbury Court, where Mr Jones was waiting to meet them.

Mr Jones said, "Welcome to your new home. Two of my men are here to help if you need anything."

Keith explained that everything would be arriving the next day.

Tony Jones asked, "Where will you sleep tonight?"

Keith said, "We are booked in at the Victory Services Club, thank you."

Tony handed Keith the keys and said, "I'll be back in the morning to introduce you to Miss Boughton, the chair of the residents association, and to show you round." He then said goodbye.

Keith and Ellen then had a good look round at the flat. It had a lovely little enclosed garden. Keith and Ellen were more than happy.

They locked the door and before going back to the club had a look round the area. It was very nice and they liked what they saw. Once back at the club, Keith and Ellen had afternoon tea and then sat in the members' lounge for a while. Sometime later they went up to their room, had a bath, watched a little television and got into bed, tired but very content.

The next morning Tony arrived around eleven and, as Keith and Ellen had done a little bit of shopping on the way in, Ellen made Tony a coffee, and he sat chatting to Keith. After coffee, Tony took Keith to meet Miss Boughton, and to show him around the block thoroughly.

A couple of hours later Keith came back with Miss Boughton to meet Ellen. She was a very nice friendly lady. She told Ellen where there was a supermarket, and she recommended a butcher and a baker. She told Keith where he could get his morning paper and also where the Doctor's was. Ellen wrote all this information down.

She asked Ellen if she had any hobbies, and when Ellen said that she liked to sew and crochet Miss Boughton said, "If you can sew, my dear, you will get plenty of work from the residents. Many of them can't sew a button on. You will be well paid if you are willing to turn up the hems of trousers and dresses."

Ellen said that she could also make and alter curtains."

"Oh good," Miss Boughton said.

Keith was to be known as the head porter, and thus his new job began. The furniture arrived, and once it was all in the flat the first thing to do was to make the bed. After more unpacking the flat began to look more like home. After yet another busy day they fell into bed, worn out but happy.

The next morning Ellen had a trip to the supermarket, butcher and baker. She bought some lovely ham, pork chops, sausages and minced beef at the butcher's. A lovely fridge-freezer had been put in the kitchen. Some cakes, rolls and a cherry pie were bought at the baker's. The rest of the groceries were from the supermarket.

Keith and Ellen were also thrilled that a phone had been put in the flat, so that evening they rang Rene and were delighted to hear that Audrey and John were there. They were very pleased to hear that Keith and Ellen were settling in well. Keith was getting on wonderfully well with his new job, and meeting more of the residents each day. On the whole they were very nice and told Keith they hoped he and Ellen would be happy at Stanbury Court.

Mr Jones had explained to Keith that he might occasionally be asked to do little odd jobs for the residents and that they would be very generous with tips, as Keith discovered two days later. During his lunch break he came to the flat for a sandwich and a cup of tea with a £50 note – one of the residents had asked him to change two light bulbs and a plug, and he had put the money in Keith's hand very discreetly.

Ellen had begun to meet the residents, and gradually she was asked to do sewing jobs and these became a regular occurrence. Ellen was being repaid extremely well.

After about a month, as Keith only worked till noon on Saturdays, after a quick lunch Keith and Ellen set off for Battersea Dogs' Home. They were going to look for a puppy. It was very exciting. They had both been brought up with dogs, and now they could have one of their own. When they got to Battersea they were interviewed about their home, where the dog would sleep and be walked. They were asked would there be someone at home most of the time? They passed the interview with flying colours. They were then taken to see the puppies. The home was lovely and clean, and most of the dogs they saw were quite happy, although one or two looked quite sad. It pulled at the heart strings; but as Keith said, "We can't take them all."

They walked through the puppy room.

Ellen said, "Oh, darling, look."

There were five adorable little black puppies.

The young man looking after them said, "They are seven weeks old – three boys and two girls."

Mongrels, they were all black apart from their paws, which were white.

He told Keith and Ellen they had been born in Battersea after the mum had been found on the streets. She was with the puppies, so Ellen and Keith could see her.

The cage was opened and they all ran out. One of the little boys ran straight to Keith and he picked him up. He was such a cute little chap that Keith and Ellen immediately fell in love with him.

They said, "Can we have this one, please?"

The young man said yes, and taking the puppy from Keith he said, "Will you both come with me?"

They were soon in a room with the vet. He checked the puppy over and gave him an injection, telling Keith he would need another one in a month.

Keith said that he would register him at the local vet's.

He was microchipped and handed to Keith, and the vet said, "What are you going to call him?"

"William," came the reply.

"Oh, I like that," he said. "Now take him home and enjoy him."

Keith and Ellen went into the shop to buy a bed, toys, harness and lead, and after making a donation to the home they got a taxi back to Stanbury Court.

William settled in very well. They only had to tell him a thing once and he remembered. He was such an obedient little boy. He met some of the residents, and one lady in particular was quite taken with him. She lived in the flat above Keith and Ellen, and from her balcony she could see William playing in the enclosed garden. She would call his name and he would look up at her and wag his tail, but he never barked.

She loved to watch him playing with his ball, and in her

lovely lilting Irish accent said, "You're a holy terror."

After six months of being at Stanbury Court, Keith and Ellen went for a Sunday evening stroll with William. They walked down Haverstock Hill towards Camden Lock, where they could walk along the towpath and stop and have a drink at a little café. When they were about ten minutes from home they heard a band playing. It soon came into view – it was the Chalk Farm Band of the Salvation Army. They were very good. There were about forty to fifty of them. Keith and Ellen stopped and listened for a while, then as it started to rain they headed off home. Ellen soon had dinner ready, and after they had eaten they settled down to watch television.

As Christmas approached Keith had a week's holiday, so they went up to Norfolk, taking William with them.

On 23 December at around 11 a.m. Miss Boughton came to the flat and gave Keith a £500 Christmas bonus. It was amazing. Keith was quite shocked.

Christmas was lovely. Audrey, John, Rene and Wilfred loved William. He was such a good little boy with Sally (Audrey and John's dog).

Back in London, Keith and Ellen agreed that the past few months had been good, and they looked forward to what 1981 would bring.

CHAPTER 9

Little William was an absolute delight. Keith and Ellen were very happy and content, and life continued in much the same way. Going to the theatre and out to dinner, they had also caught up with ex-RAF friends living in and around London.

Then out of the blue in late 1983 Keith said to Ellen, "Would you like to go to the carol service at the Salvation Army next week?"

Ellen said, "I'd love to."

Christmas was to be spent at home in Stanbury Court. They did indeed attend the carol service, which was lovely.

As 1984 arrived, one Saturday evening Keith said to Ellen, "Would you like to go to the Salvation Army tomorrow?"

Ellen said, "I beg your pardon?"

Keith said, "You heard me. What do you think?"

Ellen hadn't been to the Salvation Army in years and she said to Keith, "Would you like to go?"

He said, "I think I would."

So on Sunday evening they went to the 6-p.m. service. The corps folk were friendly and the band and Songsters were superb. After the meeting there was a cup of tea or coffee, when more people came to say hello. One of the bandsmen was born in Sheringham, so he and Ellen had a lot to talk about. The officer in charge was very nice and said he hoped that Keith and Ellen would come back again.

On the short walk home they both said how much they had enjoyed the service, and that they would like to go back.

Over the next few months Keith continued to enjoy his job. Ellen too was busy, sewing for the residents. They often went to services together at the Salvation Army.

One evening Ellen said, "It's totally different going to the Army because you want to, rather than being made to go." Somehow it felt right.

A few weeks went by, and it was announced one Sunday that a young Salvation Army officer by the name of Rachel was going to speak at the morning and evening meetings the following Sunday. She was from somewhere called Faith House, in King's Cross.

On the Sunday Keith and Ellen listened intently to what Rachel had to say about the work she and another officer did at Faith House. She spoke about the girls that worked on the streets, the runaway children, the mothers and babies and the homeless. Keith and Ellen were very interested in what she said. At the end of the evening service Rachel said that if anyone was interested to learn more, or to be a volunteer at Faith House, please get in touch.

Over the next few weeks Keith and Ellen kept talking to each other about what Rachel had said.

Keith said, "How do you feel about us volunteering at Faith House?"

Ellen said, "I'd like to find out a lot more."

Keith rang Rachel, and she said, "Can I come and see you both?"

Keith said, "Of course you can."

It was arranged for one evening the following week for Rachel to come. She told them so much more about the work at Faith House. She was very truthful about the things she told them, and some of it was hard to take in, but by the end of the evening Keith and Ellen said that they would like to volunteer at some time in the future.

Rachel said, "Ring me when you are ready."

Keith rang Rachel one afternoon in late October to say that they were ready to give Faith House a try. At last the call came through that Keith and Ellen would go down to Faith House and work with Rachel one evening in November. After a quick chat as to what to expect, the three of them left Faith House to walk the short distance to Euston Station, where they met up with the soup run.

Keith said, "Do you always get so many of them coming for soup?"

There were about fifty.

Rachel said, "We sometimes get more when it's cold and wet."

It wasn't just soup they were after. Socks, underwear, jumpers and sleeping bags were also given to people, some homeless, some down on their luck or in hostels. Keith and Ellen spoke to a young lady who said that she was nineteen and had been thrown out of home by her dad as she was on drugs. She asked for a sleeping bag and underwear, but she didn't want anything else. Ellen and Keith thought how sad it was to see a young life ruined, but this young lady wasn't the only one.

After the soup run had gone Rachel, Keith and Ellen went into the British Transport Police Station and Rachel introduced Keith and Ellen. Rachel asked if there were any runaways, and the answer was "Not tonight." Then it was through the backstreets to St Pancras and King's Cross, where there were more homeless people waiting for Rachel, once again asking for tickets for sleeping bags which could be picked up at the Salvation Army in Oxford Street the next day. One man asked for money for food, and when Rachel refused, saying, "I will buy you a sandwich," he said, "No, thanks, give me money."

Once again Rachel refused, knowing it wouldn't be used for food.

Once again they met the police at King's Cross, but there was nothing to report.

A very smartly dressed gentleman gave Rachel £20 and said, "Thank you for all the Salvation Army do."

One more stop at the newspaper stand to see Michael and June and pick up the early edition *Mail* and *Express*. Michael always gave Rachel free papers, and he gave Keith a *Mail*.

Rachel said that Michael and June were good eyes and ears.

Then it was back to Faith House. It was 1.25 a.m., but Keith and Ellen had enjoyed the experience. Rachel said she hoped that they would go again. Keith said that they would love to. They got a taxi back to Stanbury Court and fell into bed, tired out.

The next morning during breakfast Ellen said, "Wasn't it sad last night, the things we saw and heard?"

Keith agreed and said, "I'd like to go again though, wouldn't you?"

Ellen said, "Yes."

A few weeks later they went again. Rachel was on holiday, so Keith and Ellen met Sarah, the other officer at Faith House. She was a very no-nonsense young lady. They carried out the same routine as they had a few weeks before, but this time at King's Cross a young lad of about sixteen asked Sarah if she would buy him a ticket to get home to Birmingham. He said that his mum would pay the money back. Rachel bought him the ticket and sent him on his way home. A week later a letter arrived with a cheque in it from a very grateful mum. Once again Keith and Ellen found the evening full of mixed emotions.

1985 was in full swing, and in July Keith and Ellen went on holiday to Edwinstowe, in Nottinghamshire, where Keith had been brought up. The scenery was beautiful and on the way back they stopped in Norfolk for three days to pick up William, who had been staying with Audrey and John. They hadn't told anyone about the work at Faith House as they thought it would worry Rene and Audrey.

Keith and Ellen returned to London and Keith still enjoyed his job at Stanbury Court.

In October Rachel phoned Ellen and asked her if she could go to Faith House one morning to help make up food parcels and wrap toys for the families and children in B & B hotels in the surrounding area for Christmas. Ellen said that she would be delighted to help. There were toys and children's clothes spread all over the floor in the basement bedroom at Faith

House; on a huge table food was piled high. Rachel gave Ellen a list with families' names on it – i.e. mum, dad, one girl aged three, one boy aged six, etc. There were about forty families to pack and wrap for.

Ellen soon got started, and by the time Rachel brought a coffee half the list was done. By 1.30 p.m. all the parcels were finished.

Ellen got the bus home happy and content. When she got back she took William for a walk on Primrose Hill. She got home and prepared dinner. Keith finished work at four thirty and they sat together with a cup of tea. Dinner would be at 6 p.m. as usual.

Keith said, "How was your day?"

Ellen said, "Brilliant. I love helping out at Faith House. It's so worthwhile."

Keith said that he felt the same and hoped they would be asked back again soon.

On Christmas Eve they went to the carol service at the Salvation Army. It was lovely – the hall was full. The children's Nativity caused much hilarity when the little boy playing Joseph decided to change the script. It was a modern adaptation of the Nativity story. Joseph was centre stage and the Baby Jesus was lying in a Moses basket to his right. He busied himself waiting for Mary to come in.

When she arrived onstage Joseph said, "Where the hell have you been? This Baby's done nothing but f------ cry all day."

I'm sure you can imagine the uproar this caused. It was obvious that this little boy hadn't quite got the gist of the Christmas story!

Afterwards tea, coffee and mince pies were enjoyed while they were chatting to several of the corps folk. The year was coming to a close.

Keith summed the year up when he said to Ellen, "The Lord has been good to us. We really are blessed."

Ellen agreed.

Christmas of 1985 was to be spent in Norfolk – Keith and Ellen would have a week's holiday.

On their return to Stanbury Court it was back to the usual routine and the months just seemed to fly by until, one afternoon in late August 1986, Ellen received a phone call from a Mr Haskin from Select Management Ltd – the company which employed Keith – asking to speak to Keith. Ellen explained that Keith wasn't there, so could Keith ring Mr Haskin back later?

When Keith came back to the flat at four thirty he made the phone call and was asked if he would consider going to a larger block of apartments in Avenue Road, as manager, with a staff. It was much more money and a two-bedroom flat would come with the job. Keith was asked if he was willing to accept the job could he start in mid September? Keith said he would chat to Ellen and give Mr Haskin his reply within the next twenty-four hours.

After two days of talking it over Keith decided he would take the job. He rang Mr Haskin and asked if he and Ellen could go and view the flat and could they take William with them?

Over the next week things became very busy as Mr Haskin had said yes to taking William, and Keith and Ellen loved the flat, so now they would be very busy packing.

Keith and Ellen moved into Avenue Close. The flat was huge with a twenty-eight-foot lounge, two lovely bedrooms, nice kitchen and bathroom. They still continued to work at Faith House and one evening there was a phone call from the police at Holborn to ask if Keith would go to the station and act as an 'appropriate adult'.

Keith said, "Of course I will come."

This was to be the first of many, many times Keith would act in this capacity.

Ellen was still very busy crocheting for Third World babies. She also liked to write poetry on many different subjects.

They often said to each other, "We're very fortunate – we have all we need and more; we have people that love us who we love in return."

Avenue Close was very nice, but somehow it wasn't as friendly as Stanbury Court.

By now Keith and Ellen had gone into full Salvation Army uniform and were loving the work at Faith House more than ever.

Then one evening in the middle of April Rachel phoned and said, "Can I come and see you both one evening? I have got something to ask you."

Keith said, "Of course you can. Why don't you come for dinner?"

She said, "That would be lovely."

She arrived at five forty-five, ready for dinner at 6 p.m.

She began: "As you both know, Salvation Army officers move every three to five years. Well, it's coming up to the time when I will be leaving Faith House. I have had a long chat with the Army's Social Services Department about the work you both have been doing at Faith House, and told them how very impressed I have been with you both. You're most certainly a team and it's very plain to see how very much you love and respect each other, now that you have both gone into uniform. What I have to say may come as a surprise. I have been asked to ask you both if you would consider taking over at Faith House full-time and running it as you see fit."

You could have knocked Keith and Ellen down with a feather.

Keith said, "Are you serious?"

"Yes," Rachel said, "very. You would live at Faith House and William can come too." Wages were discussed, as were several other things. Rachel said, "You have a week to decide what you wish to do. Give me a call and we can go from there." She thanked Ellen for a lovely meal and said, "Before I leave we'll have a word of prayer." Then she said, "Goodnight. God bless," and left.

When she had gone Keith said to Ellen, "Do you believe what we have just heard?"

Ellen said, "No, but more to the point how do you feel about it?"

Keith said, "Excited, nervous and a bit confused. What about you?"

Ellen said, "I feel the same."

Keith said, "Let's sleep on it."

The next morning after breakfast Keith and Ellen talked about Faith House once more. It was a big step to take.

After another couple of days they had made their decision: the answer was yes. Keith rang Rachel, who was delighted. She said she would ring back soon, and true to her word about an hour later she rang back to say that Keith and Ellen had a formal interview at headquarters in Judd Street at 11.30 a.m. the next day. Keith was owed some holiday, so he took a day off.

The next morning after breakfast Keith and Ellen put on their uniforms, got the bus to King's Cross and walked the short distance to the headquarters building. The officer who interviewed them had been in training with Ellen's Auntie Kathleen, so that broke the ice for them. If they were nervous they didn't show it. They answered all the questions confidently and honestly and felt it went well.

At the end of the interview they were told, "We'll be in touch within the week."

They got the bus back to Avenue Close, got changed and took William for a walk in the park. They stopped at a little café for lunch. It was lovely.

When they got back home there was a message on the answerphone: "Please ring HQ."

So Keith did. The job was theirs. Keith rang Rachel to tell her and she was very happy for them. Ellen then rang Audrey, who was thrilled, as was Rene.

A little while later Rachel rang back to say, "You can move in on the 6th of June. Don't worry about a van – one will be arranged for you."

Keith came off the phone and said to Ellen, "We've got six weeks. Are you excited?"

Ellen said, "I am, and a little bit nervous. We have a lot to do in six weeks. Let's have a coffee, then we'll get started."

The first thing Keith did was hand in his notice. Mr Haskin said how sorry he was that Keith was leaving, but he understood. Ellen went to the post office to arrange for post to be redirected for six months, and to change her bank account. Keith would do his later. Doctors were also changed, but William's vet stayed the same. The next few weeks were very busy with packing and sorting out what to take and what to send to charity. There was very little sorting out to be done as Keith and Ellen always had a rule: if you don't use something in six months, you don't need it. They had never been hoarders.

The cottage in Bacton Road.

From left to right, Grandma Nellie, Rene, Audrey, aged fourteen,
Kathleen and darling Grandpa Jack.

Ellen, aged six months.

Ellen, aged seven, with Commissioner Edgar Grinstead.

Ellen and Keith on night patrol.

Keith and Ellen.

Ellen.

Keith being presented to HRH the Princess Royal.

Ellen being presented to HRH the Princess Royal.

Keith and Ellen at the House of Lords.

FOUNDED 1865

EVA BURROWS
GENERAL

THE SALVATION ARMY

OFFICE OF
THE GENERAL

INTERNATIONAL HEADQUARTERS
101 QUEEN VICTORIA STREET
PO BOX 249
LONDON EC4P 4EP

01-236 5222

11 July 1989

Mr and Mrs Keith Christian,
Faith House,
11 Argyle Street,
King's Cross,
London WC1H 8EJ.

Dear Comrades,

I have learnt that you are to be made Freemen of the City of London on 17 July. What a fine commendation of your work on the Midnight Patrol. My congratulations.

I trust that the ceremony will be a splendid and memorable occasion.

I have heard and read quite a deal about your work from Faith House, and it is such as would merit the commendation of our Lord Jesus Himself. May He continue to bless you in your special ministry.

Yours sincerely,

Eva Burrows

General

Camden
SOCIAL SERVICES

Social Services Dept
156 West End Lane
London N.W.6

Dear Keith and Ellen Christian,

I am writing to thank you both for the donations that you have been
able to make during the past year.

The toys at Christmas were really welcomed. The young children who
received them were delighted and the adults were relieved that
their children had something special at Christmas.

The clothes you have given us have been very useful. A young
mother in great distress was so pleased to be given such a lovely
set of baby clothes for her daughter. Some young teenagers loved
the clothes that you gave to us too.

As you are aware I work in Brent Family Service Unit as well and it
is here that many of your gifts are gratefully received.

With best wishes

Karen Salewski

Karen Salewski

ONE OF THE MANY LETTERS OF THANKS.
_____

CHAPTER 10

On the morning of the move some of the residents came to say goodbye. Mr Haskin said he had never seen a flat look so clean or smell so fresh. He said to Keith, "If ever you need a job, ring me," and then he said goodbye.

Keith handed over the keys, then Keith, Ellen and William got the bus to King's Cross and walked up to Faith House.

When they arrived the van was waiting for them. Everything was soon moved in and what furniture Keith and Ellen didn't need, the men put in the huge loft. Faith House is a five-storey Victorian house. There was a basement with a family room containing a cot, two single beds, a double put-you-up bed and a shower in the corner. There was another room set up as a laundry. On the ground floor a large hall led into a very nice lounge, a kitchen-diner and a very nice enclosed garden. On the second floor were an office, bedroom and two bathrooms; the next floor had three more bedrooms, and then up again to the loft. It was a big house, but Ellen thought, 'I'll soon have this looking welcoming and homely.' Ellen was an arctophile (teddy-bear collector), collecting mainly Harrods bears, and she thought some of them around the house would make it more friendly for children.

Rachel was there to meet them and show Keith the office. Then it was time to say, "Goodbye and God bless."

William ran up and down the stairs several times, had a look in the garden, came back indoors, got on the sofa and went to sleep. Rachel had told Keith and Ellen to settle in before starting work, so they had the one night off.

The next morning Keith opened the outer front door of Faith House at 8.30 a.m., leaving the inner door locked. Rachel had explained that the homeless regulars would come to have flasks filled and get something to eat. Other callers would arrive during the day. Sure enough at around 8.45 a.m. the doorbell rang and Ellen could see a man through the glass door.

She smiled as she opened it and said, "Good morning. I'm Ellen."

He said, "Hello. I'm Jim. Can I have a cup of tea and some biscuits?"

Ellen took his mug and she was soon back with it and a packet of biscuits.

He said, "I live over the road under the library steps. Can I come back later as usual for a sandwich?"

Ellen said, "Of course you can." Just then Keith appeared and Ellen said, "Jim, this is Keith."

Keith put his hand out to shake Jim's.

Jim said, "Oh, no one's shook my hand for years. I'm not worth it."

Keith said, "Oh yes, you are."

He shook Keith's hand and said, "Bless you, Captain. See you later." And he was gone.

Ellen went down to the laundry room to put some washing in. As she came back upstairs she thought it would be a good idea to make some sandwiches in case they were needed later. She did ham and cheese and sliced a fruit cake, then she made a coffee for herself and Keith. As they sat down the bell rang once more. It was another homeless man wanting his flask filled with coffee. His name was George. He was Jim's pal and they lived together under the library steps. He was cheerful and thanked Ellen.

After a coffee break Keith went to the bank to transfer his account. When Keith came back Ellen went to do some grocery shopping and post two birthday cards.

She wasn't gone long, and came back to find Keith happily talking to a policeman. His name was Inspector Bill Ranson and he was from Holborn Police Station. He was telling Keith about the local homeless men and women who would be regular visitors to Faith House. He also said that if Keith and Ellen needed the police they would be there for them. They had to remember that when they were on the streets on the south side of Euston Road they were under the Metropolitan Police at Holborn; on the north side of Euston Road they were under Kentish Town Police. In the stations or in the Underground they were under the jurisdiction of the British Transport Police.

After lunch it was quite quiet. Jim came for his and George's sandwiches. The flask was filled once more.

At six thirty the front door was locked as Rachel had said, "Close the door at six thirty to give yourselves some time before you both go out on what is known as the midnight patrol."

They sat down for their evening meal, and after dinner Keith took William for a walk. He had been such a good boy all day.

At 10.30 p.m. Keith and Ellen set out, taking with them the patrol bag with the tickets for sleeping bags or to get someone into a hostel if they wanted it. The route was always the same: up Euston Road, looking in all the doorways and back alleys, checking for homeless and vulnerable people who were sleeping rough and who had bedded down for the night. Then it was on to Euston Station to meet up with the soup run. As usual there were about forty or so waiting for food and clothing. Then it was on to the station concourse, where the trains came in, looking for young runaways and meeting up with the station police. Later it was down the backstreets to St Pancras, then on to King's Cross.

It was a quiet night, and by the time Keith and Ellen met Michael and June at the paper stall it was one forty-five in the early hours of the morning. Michael gave Keith *The Mail*, *The Express* and *The Star*, then it was back home to Faith House and William, hot chocolate, bath and bed. It had been such a different but rewarding day, and Keith and Ellen loved it.

A couple of days later a lovely lady named Carole came to Faith House to see Keith and Ellen. She was from Camden

Social Services. She came to talk to them about the children she would sometimes ask Keith and Ellen to take in overnight until either a foster-placement was ready or a children's home was available. She said that hopefully this would not be too often. Keith and Ellen said that they would be more than happy to help. She also spoke about the families in the B & Bs who would need food parcels and toys at Christmas. This year there were forty-nine families, and toys would be needed for sixty-three children between the ages of three months and thirteen years. She said that the parcels would need to be ready by mid November and she would provide Ellen with a list of the children's names and ages.

Ellen said, "Do you provide any of the toys and food for the parcels?"

Carole said, "No, we rely totally on you."

Ellen said, "OK, I will do my best for you."

When Carole had left, Ellen said, "I'd better see where I can get some toys for the children's parcels. After all, we don't have long – it's the end of September already." Ellen sat in the armchair and sighed. She said, "Dear Lord, please tell me what to do and where to go."

She had started writing a few ideas down when the phone rang.

Ellen said, "Good afternoon. Faith House."

A lady replied, "Oh good, I've found you at last. I'm the headmistress at the Haberdashers' Aske's Girls' School in Borehamwood and we wondered if you could use all the food from our harvest festival. We could bring it for you in the school van and perhaps you would be kind enough to tell some of our girls where the food would go."

Ellen said, "That would be wonderful. And yes, of course I would be happy to talk to the girls."

"Thank you so much."

Then it was arranged for the food to be delivered.

When Ellen told Keith he could hardly believe it. Ellen suggested that they put two large trestle tables in the basement and said, "There should be plenty of room in there."

So that's what they did.

Then Ellen rang John Lewis, Hamleys and M&S in the West End. She made appointments to see the manager at each store. She also rang Waterstones bookshop and Mothercare. By the time she came off the phone she had appointments with all of them for the following week. Time was of the essence.

During the following week the usual callers came to Faith House. Ellen made a Christmas cake and Christmas pudding. Then after breakfast on the morning of the appointments Ellen put on her uniform and got the bus into the West End, ready to go to the meetings she had arranged. She hoped to get them all done in one day and booked them at forty-minute intervals. Armed with her briefcase, a list of toys, etc., and her Filofax, she was ready to tackle some of the richest stores in the West End. As she said, "If you don't ask, you don't get."

John Lewis was first, and agreed to donate toys for children between four and seven up to the value of £350. Hamleys gave Ellen a voucher for £300. M&S said that they would give thirty toys and clothing from their end-of-season range for toddlers up to five. Waterstones bookshop would give thirty books and Mothercare would give baby clothes and toys. By the time Ellen had finished she felt it had been a very successful day.

When she got on the bus to go home she said a silent "Thank you, Lord." It was amazing how generous the companies had been, and it would all be delivered.

When Ellen arrived home she found Keith sitting on the settee having a cup of coffee with William by his side.

"Do you want a coffee, love?" he asked.

"Oh yes, please," said Ellen.

When she told Keith how she had got on he was so surprised and thrilled and said, "Well done."

After having coffee Ellen changed into her work uniform of navy skirt, white blouse and a sweatshirt with a Salvation Army crest on it. She then made a cottage pie for dinner that evening, one for the freezer, and also two dozen rock cakes and a date cake and a batch of flapjacks. The cakes were good to have in a tin for the homeless. Keith got the bag ready for later and then took William for a walk.

Jim and George came for their usual flask to be filled, and Ellen gave them some cakes and promised to fill the flask again just before she and Keith went out on the midnight patrol.

Jim said, "Thank you, my little angel. Please could you find me some socks and pants?"

Ellen said she would do her best and give them to him later, and off he went, happy.

When Keith came home with William, Ellen said, "Would you go and see if you have got any new pants and socks in your chest of drawers, please? Jim needs some."

Keith said OK, and a few minutes later came downstairs with three new pairs of pants and three pairs of hardly worn socks. He said, "We'll have to get stuff like that in, for the girls too."

Ellen agreed and said, "Let's see what deal we can do with Chris in the market on Saturday."

Keith said, "I think I could sort out a few more pairs of socks, a couple of jumpers I no longer wear and some jeans."

Ellen said, "I think I've got a few bits as well. Maybe it would be a good idea if we started a clothing cupboard in the laundry room – it's big enough."

So that's what they did.

They had dinner at 6 p.m. as usual, then had a rest before going out. It was a quiet night with only one request for a sleeping-bag ticket and only twenty-eight at the soup run. Unusually, Keith and Ellen were home and in bed by 1.30 a.m.

They both had a restful night and woke refreshed and ready for the day ahead. After breakfast the front door was opened and the day began with a visit from Jim and George. Ellen thought what dear little men they were.

This morning she said, "Why don't you two let me get you into a hostel together?"

"Oh no," came the reply, "we like being over there. We can do as we like, and you and Keith look after us."

But Ellen said, "It's going to be a rough winter and you need to be somewhere warm."

Jim said, "No, we've been on the streets fifteen years together and we like it that way."

Ellen said, "If you change your minds you let me know."

They both said, "OK."

George then asked, "Can you find me some socks and pants like Jim's?"

Ellen went downstairs and got some for him and a jumper for each of them. They were so pleased and both filthy dirty, but they both came forward and gave Ellen a hug. Keith was out with William.

Ellen went downstairs to make sure everything was ready for the school to bring the harvest produce. A few minutes later the doorbell rang. Ellen opened it and a young mum stood there, looked at Ellen and sobbed.

Ellen said, "Oh, come on, sweetheart – whatever's wrong?"

She had two little girls with her. Her name was Mary and the two little girls were Daisy and Molly. They were just three and two years old and it was clear that another baby was on the way.

Ellen said, "Come in and have a cup of tea and we can talk."

She came into the front room, into the warm. She had no coat. Ellen made a pot of tea and got some cakes. She got some warm milk for the girls and noticed that the three of them devoured the cakes as though they hadn't eaten for days.

Ellen asked, "When did you last have something to eat?"

At that very moment Keith came in with William.

"Hello," he said.

The girls loved William straight away.

It was then that Mary said, "Three days ago. I've only had milk for the girls. They haven't had any food either."

Keith instantly said, "Do you like fish and chips or burgers?"

Mary said, "I like burgers and the girls like fishcakes."

Keith said, "Right, I'll be five minutes."

Mary continued to tell Ellen that her boyfriend had gone off with her benefit money and she couldn't get any more for a week. She had no food in the flat and had run out of nappies for Molly. She began to cry again.

Keith came back with burgers, fish cakes and chips. It didn't take long for the food to disappear. Keith soon made up a food parcel containing rice pudding, custard, baked beans, tins of ham and potatoes, biscuits and cereals. He also put nappies and sanitary products in and he got a loaf of bread and some milk and butter out of the fridge.

He asked Mary, "Do you have heating and hot water in your flat?"

Mary said, "Yes, the rent and heating are paid for." Mary asked, "Can I please change Molly?"

Ellen said, "Of course you can," and she noticed the poor little mite's bottom was red-raw.

She got some cream for her, and a change of clothes. She was soaked. Ellen also found a coat for Mary and one for each of the girls.

A little while later Mary said, "Thank you so much for helping us." She loaded the food parcel, etc., into the pushchair and said goodbye.

Keith and Ellen sat down for a few minutes in the front room together in absolute silence, then Ellen said, "However will that girl cope with another baby?"

Keith said, "I don't know, but we will be here if she needs us."

Ellen cleared the dishes from the front room, and had started washing up when the doorbell rang again.

Keith answered it. It was the Haberdashers' Aske's Girls' School. The headmistress and another teacher had brought eight girls and two minibuses absolutely full to the brim with produce, toys, clothes, shoes and toiletries. There were also towels, babies' bottles and other assorted items. It was obvious these girls were from very privileged backgrounds. They were so polite, and were soon unloading the minibuses and taking everything downstairs. There was so much food that Keith and Ellen began to wonder where they would put it all. The clothes were beautiful brand-new skirts, tops, jumpers, trousers, coats and underwear, for boys and girls. There were shoes, socks, baby clothes, nappies, sanitary products and toiletries. It began to look like a shop.

Once everything had been brought in Ellen made tea and coffee and a jug of squash with cakes and biscuits for everyone. They all sat down in the front room and Ellen began to tell the group about the work that was done from Faith House, being very careful not to frighten the girls, who were between eleven and sixteen years of age. The headmistress, teacher and the girls listened intently to what Ellen had to say. They asked lots of questions. These girls had everything they could ever need and, judging by what they said, all came from loving homes. Somehow they all seemed to know how very fortunate they were – so very different from the girls Ellen had told them about.

When it was time for them to go the headmistress asked if the school could support Faith House in the future.

Ellen said, "That would be wonderful. Thank you."

Each of the girls shook hands and said, "Thank you, Mrs Christian."

The headmistress and the teacher said, "Goodbye. We will be in touch."

Ellen said, "Oh my goodness, darling, where are we going to put all these wonderful things?"

Keith said, "Let's sort it all out into boys', girls' and babies' clothes first, putting different sizes together, then we will know exactly what we've got."

Now, when Keith and Ellen first started at Faith House they were given two amazing officers – Lieutenant Colonel Stan Read and his wife Eva – whom Keith and Ellen could go to for advice. Ellen rang Eva to ask if she could help with sorting everything downstairs, and she said she would be happy to help and she would come the next day.

By this time it was around 6.30 p.m. – time for dinner. As it had been a very busy day Keith went to get fish and chips while Ellen set the table. Keith was soon back, so they sat down to eat.

CHAPTER 11

The next few weeks were very busy with making up food parcels and wrapping Christmas presents for social services and also for the mums and children in the B & Bs in and around King's Cross. Keith and Ellen were still going to the Chalk Farm Corps, and as the corps folk found out more about what Keith and Ellen did they became very supportive.

Towards the end of November Carole collected the food parcels and toys. When she saw it all she cried and said, "How can we ever thank you?"

Christmas week was very busy, with more and more young mums needing help and food. The B & Bs provided just a bed and very basic breakfast; consequently the mums and children were often hungry and had little or no money. It became more and more apparent that the situations they were in were dire, to say the least.

The soup runs were busier now winter was here. One or two of the regulars had gone into one of the cold-weather shelters, so they would at least be warm and get a good meal and the chance of a shower and clean clothes. There was also access to doctors and social services. Indeed, it was hoped some of them would find work and some sort of accommodation.

By the end of the year Keith and Ellen were shattered, but very happy and content.

The first four months of the New Year went by much the same. The routine was the same until one evening in early May.

Keith and Ellen got ready for the midnight patrol as usual,

and Ellen said, "Let's go to King's Cross first tonight."

Keith said, "Why?"

Ellen said, "I don't know. I've got a feeling."

Keith replied, "OK, darling, if that's what you want to do."

They left Faith House at the usual time and walked over to King's Cross Station, where they spoke to Michael and June on the paper stall.

Michael said, "We don't usually see you two till about two o clock. Are you both OK?"

Ellen said, "Yes, it's just that I've got a strange feeling we should go to Euston later."

They went on to the concourse to keep an eye open for young runaways or anyone else who would need help, and after a while it was time to pop into the police station. Thankfully all was quiet, so off to Euston Station they went via St Pancras and the backstreets, where they met some of the men and women who had been to meet the soup run.

They said, "Hello, Captain" to Keith, and "Hello, my angel" to Ellen.

After a chat for a few minutes they went their separate ways, and Keith and Ellen went on to Euston's concourse. They saw two of the police and had a quick word, then just waited for the last trains to arrive at around 12.45 a.m.

Ellen said, "Keith, quick – look over there!"

"What at?" he asked.

"There's a little girl all alone. Let's just wait a minute or two – we don't want to frighten her."

At that moment she walked over to Keith, tugged his coat and said, "Hello. I go to Salvation Army Sunday school."

Keith said, "Oh good. Where's your mummy?"

"Indoors" came the reply, rather indignantly.

By this time the police had come a little closer, but they just watched and listened while Keith and Ellen gave a masterclass on how to handle a little girl.

Keith asked again, "Where's Mummy, sweetheart?"

She put her hands on her hips, stamped her foot and said, "I told you indoors!"

Ellen had a try: "Where do you live, darling?" she asked.

"In a house with a red door and a six and two on it. I came for a ride on the train."

Ellen said, "OK, we had better see if we can find Mummy. She must be worried."

"No, she won't," said the little girl.

Just then one of the policemen came over and Keith said to the little girl, "Will you come home with me, then we can look after you."

She looked at Keith and said, "What's your name and the lady's name."

Keith told her and she said, "My name is Lucy. I'm six and I know my phone number."

Keith and Ellen looked at each other in disbelief.

Lucy then said, "I'll come with you if I can have some ice cream."

Ellen said, "OK," and then Keith picked Lucy up. She was very tired – it was now ten past two.

When they got home Lucy did indeed have some ice cream and a hot chocolate, and as she insisted a Wagon Wheel. This little girl was certainly precocious.

She fell asleep on the settee, so Ellen said, "Leave her there and I'll cover her up, and I'll stay in the armchair all night in case she gets frightened."

Keith sat with Lucy while Ellen went up to the office to ring the number Lucy had given her.

A lady answered the phone and Ellen said, "I'm sorry to ring you at this time of the morning. My name is Ellen and I live in London. I work for the Salvation Army and my husband and I run Faith House, a safe house for children and runaways. Do you know where your little girl is?"

"Of course I do," she said. "She's in bed."

Ellen said, "Would you please go and check?"

"Oh, for goodness' sake, I know where she is."

Ellen waited and heard a scream. "David, David, Lucy's gone!" She came back to the phone and cried, "She's gone!"

Ellen said, "It's all right – she's quite safe here with us. We found her on Euston Station coming off the train alone."

"WHAT! We'll come now. We'll drive down now."

Ellen said, "No, wait till the morning – she's fine." (Keith always checked with social services if they had a runaway that all was well at home.)

The mum said, "Thank you so much."

Then Ellen asked, "By the way, where do you live?"

Lucy's mum said, "Crewe."

Keith and Ellen later found out that Lucy had got out of bed, got dressed, went out through the kitchen door, went to the station and travelled the 147 miles to London all alone. Lucy told Ellen she had wanted a pink bicycle for her birthday and she got a baby brother instead.

The next day, when Lucy's mum and dad arrived they were so grateful to find their little girl safe and sound.

Lucy's dad said, "We are going to change the locks and put security bolts at high level."

The little family went back home taking a little bit of Keith and Ellen's love with them.

When they had gone Keith said, "Now we know why the Lord told you we should go to King's Cross first." (That was the one and only time they did the midnight patrol that way round.)

Ellen said to Keith, "That was a tough one. Thank God we found her and not one of the pimps. I dread to think what could have happened. I'll certainly be having words with that train crew tonight. They should have been far more vigilant. Now, whilst you take William for a walk I'm going to put some washing in, run the Hoover round and do some baking."

"OK, love. See you later," said Keith.

He hadn't been gone two minutes when a young lad called Mark knocked on the door. He had run away from just up the road in Edgware. He was eleven and terrified of failing his exams and what his dad would say.

Ellen sat him down for a chat, gave him a Coke and a Kit Kat and said, "Come on – it can't be that bad."

He said, "Oh, but it is. My sister is a nurse and my parents are so proud they want me to do well. But I just want to be a gardener like my dad." And he began to cry.

Keith came in with William, and Mark told Keith all that he had told Ellen.

Keith said to Mark, "Let me ring your dad, and we can talk to him."

Mark agreed.

After Keith had spoken to his dad, Mark's dad said, "All I want is for my son to be happy."

So Mark went home a much happier boy. An easy one for a change!

In early June of 1989 a lady rang Faith House. Ellen answered and the lady said, "Is that Mrs Christian?"

Ellen said, "Yes."

The lady said, "Would you and Mr Christian please bring your birth certificates, marriage certificate and passport to the City of London Guildhall at 11 a.m. tomorrow?"

Ellen was about to ask why, but the lady had put the phone down.

Ellen told Keith what had been said, and he replied, "I wonder what that's all about, Ellen. We'll find out tomorrow. I think we should go in our best uniforms,"

So the next morning, looking very smart, they got the Tube to the Guildhall and at reception they were told they were expected and someone would be down to meet them.

A few minutes later a young lady said a very cheery "Good morning, Mr and Mrs Christian. Please follow me."

They were taken into a large room with a desk and beautiful leather armchairs. They were offered tea or coffee, but they declined. By this time they were both feeling quite sick and nervous.

The young lady then said, "My name is Rebecca. May I call you Keith and Ellen?"

"Yes, of course" came the reply.

Ellen then said, "Why are we here?"

Rebecca said, "I'm so sorry – I thought you both knew. You

have both been nominated to receive the freedom of the City of London."

Keith and Ellen looked at each other.

Rebecca smiled and said, "Someone has been watching you both working on the stations, and on more than one occasion they were very impressed with what they saw, and nominated you both. All fees for you both to be made freemen have been paid, but the people who have paid for you wish to remain anonymous."

Keith said, "I don't know what to say."

Rebecca said, "It's very unusual for a couple to be made freemen together. Now all we need to do is to check your paperwork, fill in the forms and arrange a date for the ceremony to take place."

It was a lot for Keith and Ellen to take in. The date was set for 17 July 1989.

Rebecca explained the ceremony, telling Keith and Ellen that as freemen they would be able to herd sheep over London Bridge and graze their cattle in Epping Forest!

Rebecca then said, "May I be the first to congratulate you both? Well done."

Keith and Ellen said, "Thank you very much," and left.

When they got outside Keith said, "Can you believe that?"

Ellen said, "No, but isn't it wonderful? I'm so excited. When we get home I will ring Audy and Rene. You can ring your sister and headquarters."

They both had smiles on their faces all the way home.

Audrey and Rene were thrilled to think a little girl from North Norfolk was to receive the highest honour the City of London could bestow. Keith and Ellen allowed themselves to be just a little bit proud. It was unreal.

When they had changed, Keith took William for a walk and Ellen went grocery shopping.

That night Keith told King's Cross and Euston Police about the freedom. They were all so pleased for them.

At the paper stall June said, "Oh blimey! We'll have to pay to speak to you two next."

Michael just said, "Well done."

As it became known that Keith and Ellen were to receive the freedom, cards and letters of congratulations began arriving.

Keith said, "Wouldn't it be lovely if the General knew?"

Ellen said, "Yes, but she's so busy."

General Eva Burrows was a lovely lady who really cared about the Salvation Army and the corps folk. She was a rarity with such wonderful values in a modern world, and the Salvation Army could do with many more like her.

A few days later a personal letter arrived for Keith and Ellen from the General congratulating them on the freedom. This is what the letter said:

Dear Comrades,

I have learnt that you are to be made Freemen of the City of London on 17 July. What a fine commendation of your work on the Midnight Patrol. My congratulations.

I trust the ceremony will be a splendid and memorable occasion.

I have heard and read quite a deal about your work from Faith House, and it is such as would merit the commendation of our Lord Jesus Himself. May He continue to bless you in your special ministry.

Yours sincerely,

Eva Burrows, General.

That letter is a very treasured item.

17 July soon arrived and Keith and Ellen went to the City of London Guildhall for the ceremony. It was wonderful. The officials were all dressed in beautiful frock coats. The room where the ceremony took place, the Chamberlain's Court, was very ornate with beautiful pictures on the walls. There was an exquisite register that all freemen sign – an unbroken chain since 1175 with illuminated pages all written in copperplate. Keith and Ellen made their promise to the Queen and read the declaration, which reads thus:

I do solemnly declare that I will be good and true to our Sovereign Lady QUEEN ELIZABETH II; That I will be obedient to the Mayor of this City; That I will maintain the Franchises and Customs thereof, and keep this City harmless, in that which in me is; That I will also keep the Queen's Peace in my own person; That I will know no gathering nor Conspiracies made against the Queen's Peace, but I will warn the Mayor thereof, or hinder it to my power: and that all these points and articles I will well and truly keep, according to the Laws and Customs of this City, to my power.

This declaration is taken from the book *Rules for the Conduct of Life*, which is given to every person upon their admission to the freedom of the City. All fees on freedoms are devoted to the City of London Freemen's School at Ashtead Park, Surrey, to which the children of deceased freemen may be elected as foundation scholars.

Keith and Ellen then signed the register. On the page before Keith and Ellen was Prime Minister Margaret Thatcher's signature, and on the same page as Keith and Ellen was Cliff Richard's signature. After they had signed they were given their warrants, which were in a lovely Hogarth frame. It had been such a special time.

On the way home Keith said, "Aren't we blessed?"

Ellen agreed.

That night all was quiet, as were the next couple of weeks. Then in early September one of the street girls came to see Ellen and Keith. She had been on the streets since she was thirteen and was now twenty. She regularly used drugs and often had sex with men, and now she was six months pregnant. She had no money and nowhere to live and was very, very hungry. Ellen fed her, found her some clean clothes and told her to have a shower down in the family room. After a while she came back to the front room looking much better. Ellen put her dirty clothes in the washing machine.

Ellen said, "What do you want to do now? Will you go into a mother-and-baby home if I can get you a place? But you must promise me you'll come off the drugs."

She said, "I will. I know I can if I get help."

Keith came to sit with Jane while Ellen made some phone

calls. Eventually she managed to find a mother-and-baby home that would take her, but not until the following morning. Jane would work for her bed and board till her baby arrived and for ten weeks after her baby had been born. She would then decide if she wanted to keep the baby or have it adopted. The house mothers would help her to make the decision. Ellen told her all this and said she could stay at Faith House for one night. Jane was happy to do that and to go to the home the next day.

Once again Ellen phoned Liz and she said that she would go on patrol with Keith, and Ellen would stay up all night.

Ellen said to Jane, "We'd better find you some clothes, including underwear, pyjamas and shoes, and toiletries and some baby clothes. Would you like to choose some things for yourself while I sort baby things?"

Jane began to cry and said, "Why are you so kind to me? I know I've done wrong and am not worth anything. No one loves me – they never have."

Ellen said, "Now then, come on – no tears. You are worth something and I care. Now, dry those tears and see what we can find."

They were soon looking thorough the clothing store and found some nice things for Jane and the baby. Ellen found a holdall to put it all in, also putting in sanitary products. The home would provide nappies and baby milk. It was then that Jane asked Ellen if she would be her birthing partner.

The next day Ellen went with Jane to the mother-and-baby home. It was spotlessly clean and smelt lovely, although it was basic. The nuns who met them at the front door were very kind and took them to the room Jane would share with another young lass. They were then shown round the rest of the home. One of the nuns told Ellen she could visit Jane once a week on a Saturday afternoon between one and four, and Ellen said that she would come the following Saturday. She thanked the nuns, said "Goodbye and God bless" to Jane and left.

It was such a lovely day, so Ellen decided she would walk home. She thought how fortunate the young ladies in the home were to have somewhere to go to have their babies where the nuns were so kind, but for the twenty-five who were in the home there were countless others who had nowhere to go.

When Ellen got home it was lunchtime and Jim and George were on the doorstep talking to Keith.

Ellen said, "Hello. How are you two?"

George said, "Oh, we're all right. Have you got any cake?"

Ellen said, "I'll see what I can find. You'll soon look like my fruit cake."

Ellen came back with two large slices of cake, much to George and Jim's delight.

Keith said, "I wish you two would go into a hostel together. You'd have good food and a proper bed to sleep in. Please think about it."

They said in unison, "We'll think about it. See you later."

Keith and Ellen went in to get some lunch and Ellen said, "I don't think those two will go into a hostel, do you?"

Keith said, "I doubt it. They've been on the streets too long."

Ellen said, "When I've done us some sandwiches I'll hang the washing out."

Keith said, "I'll hang the washing out, then we can sit down together."

A few minutes later they were having lunch in the garden with William playing around.

Keith said, "I expect we'll hear from Haberdashers' soon. I got the list from social services while you were out – there's eighteen families and thirty-nine children this year. Do we need many toys or have we got enough in the loft?"

Ellen said, "We won't need too many. Don't forget Lego are donating and I've just got to let Hamleys know what I need, so we should be OK. We've certainly got enough clothing."

The doorbell rang. It was George, and he said, "Keith, if you can get us a hostel together we'll give it a try."

Well, you could have knocked Keith down.

Keith said, "All right, I'll try and get you in today. I'll come and tell you how I get on."

George said, "Can you find us some clothes? We've only got what we are standing in."

Ellen said, "I'll do that while Keith gets you a hostel place."

George said, "Together, mind – not separate."

George then left and Keith said, "Can you believe that at last! I just hope I can get them somewhere now."

Ellen said, "I'll go and sort out PJs, clothes and toiletries and two pairs of shoes. They are both size seven."

An hour later Keith went to tell them they had a place in Whitechapel and they would be picked up at 3 p.m. Ellen gave each of them a bag of clothes and a pair of shoes.

"Thank you, angel," they said, giving Ellen a bear hug, even though they were filthy dirty and didn't smell too sweet. The pair of them cried, shook hands with Keith and said thank you.

At 3 p.m. Ellen and Keith waved them off, hardly believing it had happened.

Ellen said, "Do you want a cup of tea, love?"

"Yes, please" came the reply.

She put the kettle on and put two pieces of sponge cake on plates. They were then both sitting in the front room.

Ellen said, "I think we can say today has been a good one."

CHAPTER 12

On 28 December the phone rang. It was the mother-and-baby home. Jane had gone into labour and wanted Ellen to be there when she gave birth.

Ellen was soon on the way, after saying to Keith, "I don't know how long I'll be."

Keith had said, "Don't worry – off you go and take care."

Twenty minutes later Ellen was at the home. One of the nuns took Ellen to one of the three delivery rooms, to Jane. She was doing well, but she looked terrified.

She told Ellen she wanted to have the baby adopted, saying, "When it's born I don't want to hold it. I want you to."

Ellen said, "Are you sure?"

Jane said, "Yes – I'll look at it, but I won't hold it. Please say you will."

Ellen looked at Jane and one of the nuns and said, "Yes."

The nun said, "You can take the baby to the nursery later if you wish."

Ellen said, "Thank you. I'd like to."

Jane's contractions were becoming more frequent, but by 10.30 p.m. – six hours later – the baby had yet to be born.

Ellen rang Keith and he said, "You do what you need to do, but get a taxi home, not the bus at this time of night."

Ellen said, "OK, darling. I love you."

Another five hours went by and at 3.18 a.m. Jane gave birth to a beautiful baby girl weighing seven pounds and four ounces. The midwife passed her straight to Ellen, who had tears in her eyes.

Jane said, "Can I see her?"

The nun said, "Yes, and you can name her if you wish."

Jane looked at the baby, but she didn't smile or touch her. She said to the nun and Ellen, "I'd like her to be Ellen Jane, if that's OK."

One of the nuns said, "Oh, that's lovely."

Jane then looked at Ellen and said, "Do you mind?"

Ellen said, "Of course not."

A little while later Jane was taken to a single room to recover. Ellen took the baby up to the nursery, where there were three other babies of various ages – two boys and another little girl. All were to be adopted. The two nuns in the nursery were much younger than the others in the home and clearly cared for the babies in their care. Ellen handed baby Ellen Jane to one of the nuns.

She said, "Oh, she's beautiful."

Ellen asked, "Will it take long for her to be adopted into a loving home?"

The nuns said, "No, our babies are usually adopted by six weeks old. In fact a couple are coming for little Toby tomorrow and he is only three weeks old. The other little boy was born yesterday and doesn't have a name, and the little girl was born on Christmas Eve. Her name is Holly Ruth."

Ellen said, "Bless their little hearts. What a start in life! Please, God, the rest of their lives will be happy. Now I'll say goodbye and God bless."

She kissed baby Ellen on the forehead, then left and went down to see the sister who was looking after Jane. Sister took Ellen into her office and told her she had found Jane a position in a large house in the country, where she could work as a kitchen maid to start with, and if she did well she could become a lady's maid. She would have a room in the servants' quarters and have all her meals and get £10 a week. Jane was now clean and off drugs and worked well and had been very respectful while she was at the home. Ellen was pleased to hear this.

Sister said, "Someone from the country house will come and pick Jane up in ten days' time." She also told Ellen that she had known the family for many years and they had been very kind to her and her younger sister.

Ellen smiled and inwardly wondered, but said nothing.

Ellen thanked her and said, "Can I say goodbye to Jane?"

Sister said, "Of course you can. I'll show you where she is."

Ellen stayed with Jane for a little while; she didn't speak of the baby, but about Jane's new job. She seemed quite happy about it all.

After about an hour Ellen said, "Do you have everything you need?"

Jane said, "Yes, thank you. One of the nuns taught me to knit, so I'm making a cardie."

Ellen said, "Well done. Be good, stay clean and work hard."

"I will," Jane said.

Ellen gave her a hug and said goodbye. It was now 8.25 a.m. Ellen had been at the home over sixteen hours, and all she wanted was to go home, have a cup of tea and sit in an armchair. Ellen said goodbye to Sister and left.

Just as Ellen got to the front door of Faith House Keith was unlocking to start the day.

He laughingly said, "Good morning. Can I help you?"

Ellen smiled and said, "I'll give you *can you help?* Put the kettle on."

Keith said, "I do love you. You look shattered. Do you want some toast?"

"Oh, yes, please," Ellen said.

She sat in the armchair, and by the time Keith brought her tea she was fast asleep. Keith left her there. He would make her another cup of tea when she woke up.

By the time Ellen woke, some three hours later, it was around lunchtime. Keith had been out with William, hung the washing out, put another lot in the machine and done some paperwork.

He said, "Hello, sleepyhead."

Ellen giggled and said, "I'll go and have a shower and change before we have lunch."

Keith said, "OK, love. I'll get lunch ready."

A little while later, as they sat together, Ellen told Keith about the time at the home and the baby and Jane's job.

He said he was pleased she was clean and had somewhere to go. "It's lovely when things work out."

That night the midnight patrol went well.

The next morning after breakfast Ellen said to Keith, "Oh, my back itches dreadfully. Will you have a look, please?"

Keith did and said, "No wonder you itch – you're covered in fleas. Go and get in the shower while I nip to the chemist."

Ellen got into the shower in her clothes and watched in horror as hundreds and hundreds of fleas fell off her. Keith soon came back with some revolting-smelling bright-green gunk, which Ellen had to shower with and wash her hair twice, some powder for the furniture, the bed and carpets, and shampoo for William. Keith locked the front door, treated the furniture and carpets, shampooed William and dried him, then went to see how Ellen was getting on. When he looked through the glass of the shower he laughed. Ellen was bright green from head to toe.

"You stink!" he said.

Ellen said, "Thanks a lot," and began to laugh as well. "Never mind – you're next."

Keith said, "No way!"

Ellen said, "Oh yes, you are."

A little while later while Ellen had a soak in some rose bubble bath Keith was glad he'd had a stinky shower as fleas were dropping off him too. They put the clothes they had been wearing in the bin.

As Keith said later, "What a palaver!"

Ellen knew the fleas must have come from George and Jim, but it was worth it really. Once the carpets and furniture had been hoovered they reopened the front door and they were ready for business once more.

Four days later when Keith opened the front door he called Ellen. George and Jim were back in their old spot over at the library. Ten minutes later they were there for tea, coffee and cakes, as if nothing had happened.

Ellen said, "What are you two doing back?"

George said, "We didn't like the hostel. We had to have a bath once a week, and bathing weakens ya! So we came back. We like it here near you."

Ellen smiled and said, "You won't get any cake till tomorrow, but I'll see what I can find."

And so it was back to the old routine.

Keith said, "Did you notice they both have new sleeping bags and they do look well?"

Ellen had discovered that George and Jim had been in the navy together, and after leaving the service went their separate ways – Jim to be a builder and George a mechanic, both in Liverpool. It seemed that after many years they had met up again when they had fallen on hard times. Thus they were still on the streets, but they insisted they were happy. They could both read, so Keith gave them a newspaper each morning with their coffee and breakfast.

Ellen once said, "Isn't it sad they don't have any family?"

In early 1990 Keith and Ellen were invited to join the Guild of Freemen of the City of London. This was the social side of the freedom of the City that dealt with functions which Keith and Ellen would be able to apply to for tickets. On 7 July Keith and Ellen went to the Tallow Chandlers' Hall to be admitted into the guild and to receive a programme of events for the year. It looked very exciting. Mr John Edwards from the *Daily Mail* contacted Keith and Ellen to come to Faith House once more to do another article for his column 'The Way It Is'.

One afternoon in August social services rang Keith to say they had a young mum with three little girls who had travelled down to London from Scotland to meet her husband and the girls' dad. He had been working in London for the past six months with a view to getting a home for his family. He had been sending money back to his wife on a regular basis, and phoned every week. He had told her just last week he was ready for them all to come to London and he had rented a house for them. Mum and girls left their rented house in Scotland and came to be reunited with her husband. There was just one problem: when the mum and girls went to meet her husband at his work she was told, "He has never worked here, love. I'm sorry – we've never heard of him."

Hence the call from social services to ask could Faith House take them in?

Keith said, "Of course we can."

So an hour later Carole arrived with mum Dawn and daughters Charlotte, Evie and Alice. The girls immediately fell in love with William. They were gorgeous little girls, so polite and beautifully dressed. Mum too was well dressed. It was very clear she cared for her children. When Carole had gone and Dawn and her girls were fed, Dawn wouldn't stop saying thank you, bless her heart. She asked if it would be OK for them all to have a bath.

Ellen said, "Of course you can. The bathroom is on the first floor – there are plenty of towels, bubble bath and shampoo."

Once again Dawn said, "Thank you."

Ellen showed them the family room, where there were toys and books.

Ellen got the girls some warm milk, and said, "Goodnight and God bless. See you in the morning. If you need me I'll be in the front room all night."

The following morning Carole from social services arrived and she said that she had been in touch with the landlord in Scotland, and if Dawn and the girls wanted to return he was more than happy for them to do so.

Dawn said, "Yes, I will go back. The girls are happy in their school, but I can't afford the fare."

Keith said, "Don't worry – we can sort that out."

Soon after lunch Dawn and the girls left Faith House. Ellen had packed food and drink for the journey, and she also gave each of the girls a book. Keith had contacted the Salvation Army in the area where the little family lived, and they would take food parcels round the following day. When they had gone, Keith and Ellen collapsed into the two armchairs with a cup of tea. It had been a very long day.

The next few days were good with no problems, and the

midnight patrols went well. Then the night after Keith had got his new spectacles a young man at Euston asked Keith for money.

When Keith said, "No, I'll buy you food, but I won't give you money," the young man punched Keith, breaking his spectacles and breaking Keith's nose. There was blood everywhere.

The police had seen it all and arrested the young man. One of the police took Keith and Ellen to the hospital and waited to bring them home. They were very supportive.

The next morning when Ellen rang headquarters Lieutenant Colonel Eva said she would come and see Keith. She told him not to go out that night.

Keith said, "The legs work; it's only the head that hurts. I'll be fine."

So after coffee with Keith and Ellen, Eva returned to headquarters, promising to return to Faith House a couple of days later. Keith and Ellen *did* go on patrol that night, but they were home by 1 a.m., in the early hours.

In September the Haberdashers' Aske's Girls' School rang to say they would be bringing the harvest produce once again. The headmistress asked if she and two other teachers could join Keith and Ellen on the midnight patrol.

Keith said, "Yes, but you must do exactly as we tell you. Wear jeans and jumpers, no jewellery and no handbags or money."

She said, "OK, we will. Thank you."

So it was arranged that they would come three nights later. When Keith and Ellen went on patrol that night they told the police at Euston and King's Cross about the teachers coming, and the police agreed as long as they stuck to Keith and Ellen like glue.

On Tuesday evening two minibuses drew up outside Faith House, and six girls, the headmistress and four teachers started carrying everything in.

Ellen said, "Wherever does it all come from?"

The headmistress said that companies in their area had heard about the collection and wanted to contribute.

Ellen said she would write a letter of thanks and send it to the school, then it could be copied and sent to the various companies. The headmistress agreed and said that would be lovely.

After a chat with the girls and teachers over tea and cakes, two of the teachers left with the girls in one of the minibuses. The others would go after they had been on midnight patrol. Shortly before 11 p.m. Jim and George came for their drinks and food. Ellen introduced the headmistress, who looked horrified at the state of them and just about managed to say hello.

As had now become the norm, George gave Ellen a hug and said, "Night night, love. See you in the morning."

Ellen and the headmistress went back into the lounge, to Keith and the teachers.

The headmistress said, "How could you let that old man hug you? He's filthy!"

Ellen said, "He may be filthy, but he's still a human being."

The headmistress said, "I couldn't do that."

It was then that Ellen said, "Whatever you are expecting to see and hear tonight, put it out of your minds. You will see many like Jim and George – some even dirtier. You will hear things you won't believe and see things you may not like, but you must not recoil or react badly. The people you will meet tonight trust Keith and me and we will not have that trust broken. If you don't think you can cope with that say so now. All we ask is that you stay close – don't wander off. If a problem arises do exactly as we or the police tell you. Now, do you have any money or jewellery on you? If so, leave it all here."

The headmistress and teachers said that they would do everything Ellen and Keith had said, so the five of them set off for Euston Station. The first stop was the soup run. There were more there than usual tonight, young and old, all hungry.

One of the teachers said, "Is this normal? They're all so hungry and some of them don't have shoes."

Ellen said, "Yes, they haven't eaten anything since last

night. They don't have shoes because theirs may have been stolen or they exchanged them for drink or drugs. Look – two of them are being given trainers now."

Ellen said a silent prayer, 'Please, Lord, don't let anything go wrong tonight.'

When the soup run had gone it was on to the concourse to meet up with the police and introduce the teachers and to keep an eye open for the pimps waiting to pick up youngsters to put into prostitution. One of the more well-known pimps was on the concourse. Keith and Ellen had seen him many times. He was a huge man and not very pleasant. He was obviously on the lookout tonight. Keith and Ellen told the teachers to stay close.

Then all of a sudden all hell broke loose. A young girl of about ten or eleven came onto the concourse. She was blonde, blue-eyed and pretty. The pimp started toward her; so did Ellen.

He saw Ellen and shouted, "Back off, you bitch."

Ellen kept going. As she got to the girl the pimp reached for the girl's arm, but Ellen got there first and held on tight.

She said, "Don't be scared, darling – it's OK."

By this time Keith and a policeman were close by watching. Keith thought Ellen could handle the situation. At that minute the pimp kicked Ellen and punched her so hard she fell.

She shouted, "Keith, get the girl."

The pimp then jumped on Ellen's hand as she lay on the floor and broke her finger. The police arrested the pimp. Keith had got the girl. Ellen got up and went over to Keith and the girl. She was on her way to meet her auntie, who had just arrived and had seen some of what had happened and couldn't say thank you enough. She said her niece, who was eleven, would never travel alone again and the pair of them left hand in hand.

Ellen's hand was throbbing now and starting to swell, but she insisted on finishing the midnight patrol. The headmistress and teachers were crying and couldn't believe what had taken place.

Keith said to Ellen, "Do you want to go home, love?"

Ellen said, "No, let's carry on. I'll be OK."

One of the policemen came over and said, "Please say you want to make a complaint, then we can get that thug off the streets for a long time."

Ellen said to Keith, "What shall I do?"

He said, "It's up to you."

So Ellen did agree to complain.

Next it was on to King's Cross, where thankfully all was quiet.

After picking up the papers it was back to Faith House for tea or hot chocolate and a chance for the teachers to talk about what they had seen and heard. They all said they were frightened at times, also sad, and couldn't quite take in what had happened to Ellen, and they started to cry again.

Ellen said, "I'm fine. I'll go to the hospital in the morning, so stop worrying."

After a little while the teachers said, "Thank you for allowing us to see a little of what you do. If there is anything the school can do please ring."

Keith said, "Thank you very much. Drive carefully. Don't have dreams. Goodnight and God bless."

It was two forty-five – early hours – so Keith and Ellen went up to bed and slept till 8 a.m.

After breakfast the next morning Ellen went to the hospital. She had indeed got a broken finger. It was taped up and Ellen was given painkillers.

When she got home Keith was out with William. Ellen put the kettle on to make a coffee and had a quick look at the paper. When Keith came back with William the three of them had some time together.

The list from social services had arrived, but as Ellen had been collecting toys from companies and shops throughout the year it would be a bit easier this time. There were twenty-one families and fifty-two children who would need food and gifts. Ellen rang Liz and asked if she could come and lend a hand. She said that she would be happy to, and her mum would come as well, so a couple of days later Liz and her mum came. There were toys, games, clothes, etc., all over the basement room. Ellen had already put names and ages on large gift bags, so all that had to be done was to wrap the gifts. Each bag would contain one large toy, two small toys, one game, one book, three pieces of clothing – underpants, socks, a jumper or a coat – and a pair of shoes for each child. The food parcels would also contain toiletries, sanitary products for the ladies, a razor and shaving products for the men. Liz, her mum and Ellen were soon making up parcels. By 11 a.m., when Keith said coffee was ready, half the bags were finished.

After a break the rest of the bags were done and Liz and her mum left, saying, "We will be happy to help anytime."

Ellen said, "Thank you. I'll be in touch."

In early December 1990 Keith and Ellen attended the Guild of Freemen banquet at the Guildhall. It was a glittering occasion with very high security. Guests entered through a guard of honour made up of the City of London Provost Company and the Honourable Artillery Company of Pikemen, all resplendent in their uniforms. Then it was on to the library for the reception and to be introduced to the Lord Mayor of the City of London and the Master of the Guild and a chance to have a photo taken, and also to mingle with other guests. After a short while dinner was announced and it was through to the main Guildhall, where the tables were set with snowy-white table linen and exquisite silver cutlery and crystal glassware. Stunning floral arrangements adorned the tables. The crystal chandeliers shone. A military band was playing in the background.

When all the guests were at their tables the Master, his lady, the City of London Lord Mayor, the Mayoress and other distinguished guests came in along with special guest speakers. When all were seated the banquet began with the finest food you could ever wish to see and eat. The head waiter just raised his hand for the waiters and waitresses to serve the 800 or so guests.

After dinner there were speeches and the Master invited one

and all to join him in the Ceremony of the Loving Cup. A loving cup containing mulled wine was placed on the end of every table, and the solid-silver loving cup was then passed from one guest to another. The person holding the cup stood with someone guarding their back, then the person in front of them removed the lid of the loving cup with their right hand, holding it high for all to see. (This symbolises that he will not strike him with his sword.) The person with the loving cup drank, the lid was replaced and the person holding the loving cup turned and passed it on, removing the lid, thus continuing down the line. All the while music was being played by the band.

One of the highlights of the evening was the rendition of the 'Post Horn Gallop', much to everyone's delight, and an encore is always wanted. On the invitations it stated 'carriages at 10.45 p.m.', when guests could purchase their photos before leaving.

All those who attended said it had been a wonderful occasion. On this very rare evening Keith and Ellen had the night off from the patrol.

Christmas 1990 was to be spent in Norfolk. On 22 December Keith, Ellen and William set off for Norfolk at 6.30 a.m. The promised snow had not arrived, so it was a good journey. They stopped at the Thetford Monument to have a coffee and to let William have a walk, and at just after 9.30 a.m. they pulled into the drive at Audrey's.

William jumped out of the car and went whizzing round the garden. It was fully enclosed, so no harm would come to him. After lots of hugs Keith took the suitcase up to Ellen's old room, then came downstairs, where Audrey had made pancakes and a pot of tea.

Audrey said, "Oh, it's good to have you two home. You look tired." Audrey noticed that Ellen's finger was still strapped. "What have you done?" she asked. When Ellen told her how it had got broken she was horrified. "Why didn't you let me know?"

Ellen said, "There was no need to worry you. You couldn't have done anything."

Audrey said, "I'd like to give him a piece of my mind. You take care of each other."

Keith said, "We're fine, Audy, so stop worrying, and let's eat these lovely pancakes."

The three of them chatted away, catching up on all the news.

Audrey said, "There's a Christmas social at the hall tomorrow evening. I got two tickets for you if you would like to come."

Keith said, "That would be nice."

And Ellen said, "It would be good to see friends – thank you."

Audrey's dog, Tina, and William came charging in from the garden, then they both lay in front of the fire and went to sleep.

Audrey said, "I've made Keith's favourite for tea – cottage pie." (In Norfolk you always had breakfast, dinner, tea and supper. It was considered posh if you had breakfast, lunch and afternoon tea and dinner.)

A short while later Rene came down. She looked very poorly. Although she insisted she was all right, Ellen had her doubts. Once again the question arose about Ellen's finger. Rene made it very clear what she thought about it. Rene never swore in her life, but people knew by the look on her face what she was thinking. Audrey said that John would be home from work at 6 p.m., then Wilfred, who was now retired, would join them all for tea.

The little cottage looked lovely. There was a beautiful Christmas tree in the front room, and a lit star was hanging in the window. There were presents under the tree and a Nativity scene was in the centre of the sideboard. Ellen's mind wandered back to the many wonderful childhood Christmases with her beloved grandpa, Jack. She still missed him.

Some more time was spent chatting. Rene and Wilfred were now living in a flat in Hall Lane, next to the Salvation Army Hall, and they loved it. Keith and Ellen were glad they were nearer town and Audrey. Auntie Kathleen was now at a corps in Norfolk, so the three sisters met up on a regular basis.

John arrived home from work and said to Keith, "Hiya. How are you?" He said, "Hello, Ellen," and gave her a hug.

She said, "Hello, Uncle" – a private joke between the two of them. They teased each other all the time and loved it.

Yet another question arose about the finger.

Once John had washed and changed, Wilfred had arrived and Audrey served tea. As always it was yummy.

After tea was finished John and Keith took the dogs for a walk while the ladies washed up. Wilfred sat in the armchair and went to sleep. Ellen went upstairs and brought presents down to put under the tree. When John and Keith came back a lovely evening was enjoyed by all.

Just after 10 p.m. Rene and Wilfred walked the five minutes home, then Keith and Ellen had a bath, said goodnight and went up to bed. It had been a lovely day.

Keith and Ellen slept till nine fifteen the next morning. As John was now off work till after the New Year he had taken Tina and William out. It was beginning to snow. Ellen was quite excited.

After breakfast she put her coat and gloves on and set off for the cemetery to go and visit Grandy's grave. On the way back Ellen saw her friend Susan, so they stopped for a chat and wished each other a happy Christmas.

Later in the morning Keith and Ellen popped into town and picked up the turkey Audrey had ordered along with a joint of pork, chipolatas and bacon. They also got the veg for Christmas Day.

When they had finished they went to see Rene and Wilfred for coffee and a mince pie. They took Rene some flowers and had also got some for Audrey. Rene would be going to the social later, but Wilfred would not.

After a little while Keith and Ellen went back to Audrey's with the shopping. Audrey suggested that John could go and get fish and chips for dinner at around 1 p.m. as there was to be a buffet at the social later.

Later in the afternoon Audrey and Ellen prepared as much as they could towards Christmas Day. All the family would be at Audrey's, and Audrey would cook the turkey on Christmas Eve, as she always did. Ellen started putting the finishing touches to the Christmas cake. She had got three exquisite little glass angels from Harrods to put on it. They had tiny gossamer wings and little gold halos. Keith and John had gone out, so Audrey and Ellen sat down and chatted. Ellen loved this time with Audrey. She was an amazing auntie and loved Ellen unconditionally.

Keith and John returned, so the four of them sat down for a cup of tea. It began to snow again.

Ellen said, "Wouldn't it be lovely if it snows on Christmas Day?"

The social was to start at 7 p.m., so the four of them set off for the hall at around six thirty. The hall had been decorated with a tree and the Sunday-school children had made paper chains to go all the way round the hall. There was a large stable on the stage, ready for the Nativity play that would take place on Christmas Eve. Rene was already there. She looked so very, very ill that Ellen was sure something was wrong, but she didn't say anything. There were a lot of Ellen's old friends there. It was good to catch up. Some of them had children, and it was lovely to see them.

The social began with games for everyone to join in if they wished. There was a quiz all about Norfolk and, for the children, hunt the Christmas present.

At the end of the evening everyone helped tidy the hall ready for the next evening's play. The ladies washed up. It had been a most enjoyable evening. At 10.30 p.m. everyone said goodnight and went their separate ways. Audrey, John, Keith and Ellen said goodnight to Rene and went back to Audrey's. They were soon in bed and fast asleep.

When they awoke on Christmas Eve everything was covered in snow. It looked lovely. Tina and William went out into the garden. They loved the snow, running around, trying to catch the falling snowflakes.

After breakfast Ellen said to Audrey, "Come and make a snowman."

Audrey looked at Ellen, smiled and said, "Oh, come on, then."

John and Keith laughed and said, "You two are crackers. We're going to have a coffee and put the turkey in the oven."

Audrey and Ellen had great fun, giving the snowman coal eyes and mouth, and a carrot nose. Ellen went indoors and got one of John's caps and put it on the snowman's head, and put the yard broom in his hands. He looked really good.

Audrey and Ellen came in to get warm and have a hot chocolate, and just then John looked out of the window and said, "What's my bloomin' hat doin' out there?"

Ellen laughed and said, "It'll soon get dry by the fire."

John just smiled and said, "Huh!"

Keith and Ellen walked up to Rene and Wilfred's, then they went into the church. It looked beautiful. The huge Christmas tree was lit, and there was holly on the ends of the pews and wonderful flower arrangements in red and gold. The Nativity scene was at the front of the church, but the figure of Baby Jesus wouldn't be put in until midnight Mass.

When Keith and Ellen came out of the church the Salvation Army band was playing in town, so they stopped to listen for a while. Then it was back to Audrey's. The smell that was coming from the kitchen was lovely – the turkey and pork were cooking and the veg was in the pantry in bowls on the marble cold slab; it was so cold in there that ice was forming on the water. Audrey had made a cheese-and-bacon pie for tea; they would have eggs on toast for dinner.

After dinner the four of them sat and chatted together – or rather, Audrey and Ellen did. John and Keith fell asleep in the armchairs.

In the evening Audrey and Ellen went to the Nativity play while John and Keith stayed at home. The play was lovely – all the children did very well. At the end Father Christmas came and gave all the children a small gift.

As he left he said, "You must go home now, and go to bed and go to sleep so I can visit your house later."

The children sang 'Jingle Bells' and Father Christmas was gone.

Audrey and Ellen made their way home, where they watched

some television with John and Keith.

Just before 11 p.m. Ellen said, "Listen."

Audrey smiled and said, "What?"

Ellen said, "I can hear the band."

Audrey said, "Yes, I knew they were coming. I thought it would be a surprise."

By now the band were in the front garden. It was like old times. They played 'Once in Royal David's City', 'Silent Night' and 'Away in a Manger'. It was lovely.

Ellen said, "Thank you so much," and wished them all a very happy Christmas.

Audrey and Ellen went back indoors, said goodnight and went to bed.

Christmas-morning breakfast was always bacon, egg, toast, orange juice and coffee or tea. The pudding was put on to steam, the veg were in the saucepans and the turkey and pork were carved and ready. Christmas Day dinner would be served at 1 p.m. and the gifts would be exchanged later.

A Christmas Day service was on the television, and Audrey and Ellen sang along with the carols. John was very cheeky and asked Audrey and Ellen if they were in pain as they were making such a dreadful noise.

Audrey said, "You cheeky little beggar!" and laughed.

Rene and Wilfred arrived at 12.30 p.m. Even Tina and William had Christmas dinner.

After the washing-up was done, everyone had tea or coffee, then they went into the front room, where gifts were exchanged. At 3 p.m. the Queen's speech was listened to. A lovely afternoon was enjoyed, and at teatime all that they wanted was a piece of Christmas cake. It had been a truly wonderful Christmas.

On 28 December Keith and Ellen walked up to Rene and Wilfred's to say goodbye, then went back to Audrey and John to pick up William and the car ready for the drive back home. There were a few tears when Audrey and Ellen hugged each other.

Audrey said, "You take care. Ring me when you get home."

And John said, "No more broken fingers."

The roads were not too busy until the outskirts of London, then it took an hour and a half to do the last twenty miles.

The first thing Ellen did when they reached home was to ring Audrey as promised. Then she put the kettle on for a cup of tea. A friend had got milk and a loaf of bread. They had hardly sat down when the doorbell rang. It was George.

"Oh, we've missed you. No one can make a cuppa like you two can. We missed your cakes too."

Ellen said, "You'll have to wait until tomorrow for cakes. I'll give you some biscuits for now."

George then said, "Where's your proper clothes? You don't look like my angel in these ones."

Ellen was in a blue dress and cardigan, not in uniform.

She laughed and said, "You'll still want your flask filled."

"'Course I do."

So Ellen filled his flask and found a packet of biscuits, and he was gone.

Ellen and Keith sat together with William, who was on his bed with his teddy bear.

Ellen said, "Are you hungry, love, or shall we have something on toast for dinner?"

Keith said, "That would be lovely."

Ellen went to put some washing in the machine while Keith unpacked the cases, then they sat down for a rest before going out on midnight patrol. Keith took William for a walk. It was bitterly cold, so William needed his dog coat on.

Sometime later the post was checked, but there was nothing exciting.

CHAPTER 13

In 1992 there was a particularly cold January and the nights were bitter. The cold-weather shelters stayed open so that those who wanted could have somewhere warm to stay. How Ellen wished Jim and George were still in the warm! They were both elderly and vulnerable. They continued to collect tea, coffee and cake, etc., two or three times a day, always saying thank you, then one bitterly cold lunchtime in mid February they were late.

Keith said, "Don't worry, love – they'll be here soon."

When they didn't come Keith went across the road and found them both. They had died.

Ellen cried when Keith came back: "It's so sad – they could have been anyone's grandpa."

Keith rang the police and they arranged for an ambulance, but of course it was far too late. The undertakers came and took Jim and George away. The funeral was a very sad occasion, with just a vicar and Keith and Ellen. They were both cremated.

Some five months later, in July, the doorbell rang and two ladies were on the doorstep. Keith had answered it.

They had a beautiful bouquet of flowers, and one of them said, "Could we come in and speak to Ellen, please?"

Keith took them into the welcoming front room and called Ellen, who was doing the ironing in the laundry room.

When Ellen came upstairs they gave Ellen the flowers and said, "We are George and Jim's daughters."

Ellen said, "Forgive me, but what did you say?"

Once again they said, "We are George and Jim's daughters."

Keith said, "I'll put the kettle on."

Over a cup of tea Mary and Joyce told Ellen and Keith that their two families had lived next door to each other for many years, each couple having just one child – a daughter. They were both loving families where the wives stayed at home and the husbands worked hard to provide for their loved ones. The girls grew up and left school – one trained to be a teacher, the other a nurse – and eventually both girls married and left home. When the girls' mothers died the husbands, George and Jim, couldn't cope, so after eighteen months, and now retired, they just upped and left, not saying where they were going. For years the girls tried to find them to bring them home, but to no avail, then five months ago they found out that George and Jim had died and they heard how kind Ellen had been to them, and also what Keith had done. They wanted to say thank you. They said to Ellen, "Please will you tell us a little about our dads?"

Tears were streaming down Ellen's face and she said, "We had no idea. We just knew two dear little private elderly gentlemen who came every day for tea, coffee and cake, and occasionally clothing and shoes."

Mary said, "Did they ever ask for money?"

Keith said, "No, never."

Joyce said, "We don't know how to say thank you enough for looking after our dads. Please accept this." And she gave Ellen an envelope with a very generous donation inside. The ladies then asked Keith if he would show them where their dads had lived before they left for home, which of course he did.

After Mary and Joyce left, Ellen said, "Oh, my darling, it doesn't get any easier, does it?"

Keith said, "No, but we made a difference in George and Jim's lives, bless them."

August and September were relatively normal, except that Keith and Ellen had been to dinner at the House of Lords with the Guild of Freemen and had a lovely evening with dinner in the peers' dining room.

At the end of September they had five days in Norfolk. They relaxed as soon as they arrived in that beautiful part of the world, with clean fresh air and peace.

Rene told them she had cancer in her back and spine and that nothing could be done. She said, "Don't you dare cry – I'm in God's hands and I'm not worried."

It was a shock, to say the least.

Despite this sad news, Keith and Ellen enjoyed their break and William enjoyed the walks on the beach and through Bacton Woods, then all too soon it was time to go back to London with the promise that Audrey would ring if they were needed. Sometimes life sends things our way that are hard to deal with, and without faith and God's love we just couldn't cope. God had been very good to Keith and Ellen over the years and He still was.

Over the time that Keith and Ellen had been at Faith House many of the mums would come and visit, often just for a chat or to say they were expecting another baby.

Ellen used to say, "Why did you get yourself in this situation?"

The girls would reply, "Oh, I know he loves me if we have sex."

Ellen said, "That's not love, sweetheart. Where will he be when the baby comes along?"

But she knew she was knocking her head against a brick wall. All she could do was be there when she was needed.

One evening at the end of November Keith and Ellen left for midnight patrol as usual, hoping for an easy night. There was a young lady of the night sitting on a wall eating fish and chips while having sex with a client.

As Keith and Ellen went past she called to Keith, "Hi, Pops. I'm having a working dinner."

Keith and Ellen couldn't help but laugh with each other.

Keith said, "Wash your hands when you've finished." He then turned to Ellen and said, "Whatever next?"

They continued on and thankfully it was a quiet night. They picked up the papers at King's Cross and headed for home.

Just up the street Keith said, "Stop – there's something on the doorstep. Stay here."

Ellen watched and waited, and Keith soon beckoned her to join him. Inside a crisp box was a tiny newborn baby wrapped in a grey jumper. Keith took the box indoors and Ellen followed. She took the baby out of the box. It was a little boy clearly just a few hours old. On his jumper was pinned a note. Ellen gave it to Keith so she could see to the baby.

The note said, 'Dad and Mum please take care of my baby. I can't. You will find him a home where he will be wanted and loved.'

Keith said, "I'll ring social. It's 1.35 a.m., but there'll be someone there. I'll ring the police as well."

Ellen said, "By the noise this little one is making he needs changing, a clean Babygro and a feed."

The baby was soon having a bottle.

The police arrived at two fifteen closely followed by Carole from social services. The police said they were happy for Carole to do what was needed and left.

Carole said, "We've got a duty doctor on call. I'll see if he can come and give the baby a once-over, if that's OK."

Keith said, "Yes, please."

Half an hour later the Doctor arrived and said the baby was fine and was clearly being looked after. Carole made another phone call and told Keith and Ellen she couldn't get the baby a foster placement till the next morning, as there was nothing available. So would we keep him overnight.

Keith said, "Of course we will."

When Carole had gone, Ellen said, "We see so much poverty and sadness everyday, then for one night we sit and dine with people who are multimillionaires and billionaires. Most of them have no idea what goes on."

Keith said, "I know, sweetheart, but money doesn't buy happiness."

On 28 December friends were coming from Norfolk to have a few days with Keith and Ellen. They were a Christian couple, so Ellen had got tickets to take them to the midnight service at St Paul's Cathedral on New Year's Eve. It was a wonderful experience with a Salvation Army band and the cathedral choir. The cathedral was full. At midnight the bells were rung. Keith and Ellen's friends were thrilled.

They also went to Petticoat Lane.

Keith took the husband on the midnight patrol. He was appalled and saddened by what he had seen and maybe a little bit scared when Keith took him into Lincoln's Inn Fields.

Four days later, when they left, he said to Keith and Ellen, "You two, stay safe. I'll worry now."

Keith said, "We'll be fine."

Late in January 1993 the police brought two young brothers to Keith and Ellen late one evening. They were thirteen and fifteen and had got lost on a day out in London. Their parents in Birmingham had been contacted and their dad would come and collect them the following morning. Could they please stay at Faith House overnight and be safe?

Keith said, "Of course they can."

Ellen rang Liz to go on patrol with her, and Keith would stay with the boys. They were both very polite and clean, but hungry. Keith went to get them burger and chips. They loved William and played with him, and asked Keith if they could watch television before bed. Just before eleven Liz arrived to go out with Ellen. Keith would stay up till Ellen got back safe, then they would both go to bed as the boys were old enough that neither Keith nor Ellen need stay up all night. It was an exceptionally quiet patrol, so once Liz had got a taxi home Ellen was back just after midnight.

At seven thirty the next morning Ellen started breakfast, then knocked on the boys' bedroom door. There was no answer, so she called Keith. He knocked again. No reply, so he opened the door. The sight and smell that met Keith and Ellen was horrendous. The boys had gone, but in the night they had gone to the toilet and spread poo everywhere – over the beds, curtains, carpet and all the bed linen – also over a chair.

Ellen cried. Keith was angry – he called the police to say the boys had gone. The policeman said that, more by luck than anything, they were caught trying to steal a drink in the station and were now in custody.

When Keith told him what they had done he said, "Their dad is on the way. Don't touch anything. When he gets here I'll bring him over with the boys and they can face the music, and clean up the mess they made."

A few hours later two police officers, the boys and their dad arrived.

The police said to Keith, "Would you please show us the room the boys were in last night?"

Keith took them upstairs, and when he opened the door the police and the dad made a comment I cannot repeat here.

The police turned to the boys and said, "Did you two do this? If so, why?"

The eldest boy said, "Yeah, we were bored so we thought it was a laugh."

Their dad said – or rather shouted – "A laugh? I'll give you something to laugh about. When you get home you're grounded for six weeks, no pocket money for a month and no TV either."

One of the policemen said to the dad, "Can I talk to you alone for a minute?"

When they came back the dad said, "Mrs Christian, do you have rubber gloves, bucket, bleach and cleaning products?"

Ellen said, "Yes."

The dad then said, "While I supervise, these two are going to clean this room until it shines."

The youngest boy said, "No, Dad, it stinks and we'll get dirty."

Their dad said, "You should have thought of that. Now get started by stripping the beds. Mrs Christian will show you where the washing machine is. Hurry up – I've had to take a day off work because of you two."

The police officer said to Keith, "Do you want us to do anything?"

Keith said, "No, I think they have learnt their lesson."

The policemen went to leave and the boys' dad said, "Thank you so much. I can't believe what my boys have done. I'm so sorry."

The policeman said, "It's your boys that need to apologise, not you," and he left.

The boys were getting on with the cleaning. With the window open the smell began to ease. They had taken the curtains down and put them in a black bag. Their dad insisted on paying the dry-cleaning bill. He was such a nice man. Ellen made coffee and took one to the boys' dad.

The boys said, "Can we have a drink, please, Mrs Christian?"

Their dad said, "They can have water." He was certainly not giving the boys any leeway.

By lunchtime the beds had been remade, the chair was clean, and all that had to be done was to clean the carpet. It was fortunate that Ellen had a carpet-cleaning machine. Ellen had made sandwiches for lunch for everyone. After lunch the cleaning continued. Ellen had to admit the boys had done a good job. They looked worn out and it had been so unnecessary. It was clear they had a good home, but sadly, like many teenagers, didn't appreciate it. By late afternoon the boys had finished. They came downstairs with their dad.

He said, "I think you two have something to say to Mr and Mrs Christian." The eldest boy looked at his dad, who said, "Go on – I'm waiting."

The eldest boy spoke. He said, "We're really sorry for what we did. We know now it wasn't funny. It was hard work cleaning. We didn't think Dad would make us do it. We won't ever do anything like that again. We are sorry. Mr Christian, will you ask Dad not to ground us for six weeks? We won't see our mates."

Their dad said rather sharply, "If you complain I'll put it up to eight weeks."

The boys said no more.

Keith said, "Have you learnt your lesson, boys?"

They both cried, "Yes, we have."

Keith said, "OK, but I think your dad is doing the right

thing. Make sure you behave yourselves or you will end up in far bigger trouble."

"We will behave," said the youngest. "I am sorry."

Their dad said, "Thank you, Mr and Mrs Christian, once again. I can't say how sorry I am. Now, you two, get in the car. I dread to think what your mother will say."

The boys said, "Please don't tell her, Dad."

He said, "I'm not going to – you are. Now get in the car before I lose my patience."

And they were gone.

Ellen said, "Oh, darling, what a performance! Little beggars – I could have screamed, but wasn't their dad nice?"

Keith said, "Yes, but I don't think it's going to be a very good journey home. Now let's get fish and chips for tea, then we can have a rest before patrol."

A couple of weeks later Keith heard that he was to receive the Chief Superintendent's commendation from the Metropolitan Police at Holborn. It was unknown for a civilian to receive the commendation. It reads thus: 'For unwavering commitment to police and the community by acting as an "Appropriate Adult" on various occasions in a voluntary and unpaid capacity.' The commendation was presented by the Chief Superintendent at Holborn Police Station. Ellen was so very proud. Afterwards a celebratory lunch was attended by police colleagues and friends.

Another wonderful evening in the Guild of Freemen's calendar is the Ceremony of the Keys at the Tower of London. This ceremony has taken place every night for 700 years. It has never been cancelled and was only delayed when a World War II bomb knocked two wardens off their feet. At exactly 2152 hours the Chief Yeoman Warder comes out of the Byward Tower. He carries a lantern in one hand and the Queen's keys in the other. The foot guards escort him to Traitor's Gate. All guards salute the Queen's keys. He locks the gate and goes to the Bloody Tower, Tower Archway, where a sentry waits.

The challenge rings out: "Halt. Who comes there?"

"The keys," replies the Chief Yeoman Warder.

"Whose keys?"

"Queen Elizabeth's keys."

"Pass Queen Elizabeth's keys. All's well."

The escort presents arms, then the Chief Yeoman Warder raises his Tudor bonnet high in the air and says, "God preserve Queen Elizabeth."

The guards reply, "Amen."

Exactly as the clock chimes 2200 hours the bugler sounds the last post on his bugle. The Chief Yeoman Warder takes the keys back to the Queen's house. The guards are then dismissed. Visitors are escorted out at 2205 hours. No mobile phones are allowed in and no photos are allowed. However, this is truly a unique experience.

The next few months went by without incident and life was good. Keith and Ellen went up to Nottinghamshire and enjoyed every minute. They soon got back into the same routine and the usual Christmas preparations got under way.

In November Keith and Ellen attended the Lord Mayor's Show. They were fortunate enough to have seats in the stands by St Paul's Cathedral. It was a dry day and the atmosphere was lovely, nobody knowing quite what to expect. The event began with the guild's chaplain, the Dean of St Paul's, leading the assembled company in an act of remembrance for the fallen. Then the show began. There were numerous military bands, floats of all kinds depicting many trades – grocers with their colourful fruit and veg, tailors with beautiful suits – dogs from Battersea Dogs' Home, fire engines, Gog and Magog (the protectors of the City), cheerleaders and numerous others, including carriages from the livery companies. Then came the Guild Master, who gave a very hearty wave, then the highlight of the show – the new Lord Mayor, resplendent in his robes, travelling in his beautiful golden coach.

After the procession members of the Guild of Freemen and their guests enjoyed a sumptuous four-course lunch before departing for home, having had a thoroughly enjoyable day.

One evening, just before Christmas 1993, Keith and Ellen were in King's Cross Station talking to a young couple waiting for their train. They were both smartly dressed and just wanted to talk about the Salvation Army and its work.

The young man said, "I'm Sam and this is my wife, Grace. We've just been to the Royal London Hospital for a check-up. Grace is expecting quads."

Keith and Ellen said, "Congratulations. How lovely for you! You will be busy."

Just then Grace fell off the bench she was sitting on on to the floor. Keith immediately rang for an ambulance. Sam looked terrified. The ambulance arrived very quickly and Sam went with Grace to hospital.

In February 1994 Keith and Ellen received a letter to say Grace and Sam now had four very healthy babies – three girls and a boy – all doing well, thank God.

CHAPTER 14

At the start of 1994 life was good for the Christians and they counted their blessings every day, saying, "God is good. We are so grateful for all we have."

Audrey, John, Rene and Wilfred had all been to stay with Keith and Ellen. Audrey and Rene loved London, but John and Wilfred were not so keen. Audrey worried about the work Keith and Ellen did, so they decided not to tell her how many times they had been hurt. After all, she couldn't do anything about it. Rene was now becoming increasingly poorly, but she said she had no pain, which was a blessing.

She said, "The Lord doesn't want me yet."

In the Easter of 1994 Ellen became very unwell, but no one could find out why. One day she saw a different doctor and he said that Ellen was very anaemic and exhausted. He said that she must have complete rest with no patrols for at least three weeks.

Ellen said, "I can't – my young mums and the other young people need me. I'll have a week, but then I must go back on patrol. I promise I'll have one night off a week."

The Doctor said, "OK, you make sure you do, my girl."

So she did, much to her annoyance, and after about six weeks she began to feel much better.

During the summer a phone call came from a very influential businessman in the city asking if there was anything needed at Faith House.

Keith said, "We could use baby clothes as more and more mums are asking for help."

He said, "OK, Mr Christian – I'll get back to you in a few days."

The next week went by, then the same businessman rang to say he had a few baby things and could he bring them the next day? When he arrived in a Rolls-Royce followed by a driver in a van Keith and Ellen just looked at each other.

"Hello," he said. "Can my man unload the van while I empty the car?"

"Certainly," Keith said. "I'll give your man a hand."

We could have set up a shop with what he brought. There was a brand-new cot absolutely full of baby clothes, all brand new, a beautiful cream pram/pushchair, a high chair, babies' bottles, two sterilisers, baby food and dozens and dozens of packs of nappies.

When everything was brought in, the businessman asked if he could look round.

Keith said, "Yes, of course you can."

A little while later this lovely man said goodbye, adding, "If you need anything let me know."

Keith thanked him for his kindness and came back indoors.

Now, you can call it fate or fortune, but what happened next was amazing. Keith and Ellen like to think it was all in God's plan. A young couple, Paul and Laura, whom Keith and Ellen had been supporting for over a year in one of the B & Bs, had a little girl of four and a new baby on the way. Paul worked as a builder and they had been offered a three-bedroom house in Camden Town. They had saved money for second-hand beds, a cooker and a fridge, but they couldn't afford a cot. Could Ellen find them a second-hand one? They were such a lovely young couple and Paul worked so hard.

Ellen said, "We can do better than that – we can find you a new cot, a pram, baby clothes and other bits, but, Paul, you will have to collect them."

He said, "Oh, thank you. I will."

Two weeks later Paul and Laura collected everything the day before the move.

Laura said, "Please come and see us in our new house."

Ellen said, "I will. Now off you go and take care."

Keith said, "Do you know, darling, we couldn't have planned

that if we had tried. I love it when something like that happens."

As the years went on the work at Faith House continued. One evening in late November Ellen and Liz were on patrol together as Keith had an RAF reunion dinner to attend. When Liz and Ellen approached Euston Station they could see three lads coming towards them, but they didn't worry as Ellen knew one of them. His name was Mark and he often met Keith and Ellen at the soup run. As they got nearer the lads began to run towards Liz and Ellen. There was nowhere for them to go, so they just kept walking. As they got level with the lads, one of them kicked Liz. She fell and hit her arm.

One of the others went for Ellen, saying, "Where's the money?"

Mark said, "Do you carry money?"

Ellen said, "We don't have money. Keith is the one who brings money."

He got hold of Ellen, tore her jacket and screamed, "You bitch – give me money!"

Liz was frightened.

Ellen said, "I do not have money – now let us go."

One of the lads flew into a rage, knocked Ellen down, kicked her, broke four ribs and gave her a bloody nose.

Mark shouted, "Leave them alone."

At that moment a man and woman saw what was going on and came to help.

Ellen said to Liz, "Are you OK?"

She said, "Let's get back to Faith House."

So they slowly made their way back. It was quarter to midnight. Keith had been home half an hour. When he saw Liz and Ellen he was horrified.

He asked, "Whatever happened to you two?"

Ellen said, "Make us a cup of tea first, then we'll tell you. We're a bit sore, but OK. Liz hurt her arm and my ribs have been broken again."

Liz said, "Do you mind if I go up to bed? I'll have a bath first. Don't you ever tell my mum."

Keith said, "Night night, love. God bless. See you in the

morning." He turned to Ellen and said, "Let's get your poor face cleaned up and tell me what happened."

When Ellen had finished Keith said, "You can't keep getting beaten up, sweetheart."

Ellen said, "I love my job. We'll just have to be more careful."

Keith said, "Let's just get you to bed. Do you want a bath?"

Ellen said, "Yes, please, if you'll help me get in and out." She cried as she got up – it really hurt.

The next morning, being Saturday, Keith got breakfast for himself and Liz. Ellen was still asleep. Liz assured Keith that she was OK and set off for home around 10 a.m. Keith went upstairs to Ellen, who had a lovely black eye.

She said, "Morning, darling. Will you help me get dressed? Then I can come down for breakfast."

Keith said, "I'll help you get dressed, but you're not to try and do anything. You can sit on the settee and read a book or talk to me and William. We're not going on patrol tonight – it's getting bad out there and it's worrying me."

Ellen said, "I know, love, but worry won't make it any better."

By the end of the year Ellen's ribs were healing well, although it still hurt if she laughed or coughed. 1994 hadn't ended well. Keith and Ellen hoped that January would be the start of a good year.

However, it was not to be as in January 1995 Wilfred had a massive heart attack at home and went to heaven. His funeral was held at the Salvation Army in North Walsham and he was buried in the cemetery in Bacton Road.

Next was a visit to Clarence House, the home of HRH Prince Charles. Twenty guild members had been invited. It was wonderful. The rooms were exquisite – a truly unique experience.

One morning after breakfast Keith said, "Isn't it lovely? We've not had any problems for over a fortnight."

Ellen said, "Don't you speak too soon. I like it this way, and you may be tempting fate."

The doorbell rang and a girl of about twenty stood there with a police officer. She had with her a baby boy who was so tiny.

The police officer said, "Hi, Keith. Can we come in, please?"

Keith said, "Of course you can," and took them into the front room.

The girl's name was Susan. Her hand was heavily bandaged and she looked terrified.

Steve, the policeman, said, "Can I leave Susan and her baby with you, Keith?"

Keith said, "I'll show you out."

When they got to the front door, Steve said, "This is a difficult one, Keith. Good luck."

Back in the front room Susan had told Ellen the baby was called Andy. He was five weeks old. Judging by his cry, he was either wet or hungry. Ellen prepared a bottle for Andy and changed him. Once he was comfortable and fed he was soon fast asleep.

Susan said, "I'm nineteen and the policeman said I can tell you anything."

Ellen said, "You can, love, but let's get you some tea and something to eat."

Keith said, "Is soup OK?"

"Oh yes, please," Susan said. William was sitting at Susan's feet and she began to relax a little. Susan said, "I had a boyfriend in Bolton, half Greek, half Spanish, and we'd been together two years. Then I had Andy. He got jealous and hit me a few times. Then two days ago he came home from work when his dinner wasn't on the table. He grabbed me, put me in a headlock, put my hand on the worktop and chopped one of my fingers off with a carving knife. He just laughed and left. I wrapped my hand in a towel, put some things in a bag, put Andy in his pushchair and ran. I made up a story at the hospital so I could get my finger looked at and got a train – I didn't care where to. And when I got off the train here Steve saw me and asked if I was OK. I told him what I've told you, and he said you might be able to help me. I've got £52.60 savings in my purse and one change of clothes for me and Andy. I daren't stop and get any more."

Ellen said, "We can find you and Andy clothes, so that's no problem."

Keith then said, "Do you have anyone you could stay with?"

Susan said, "No. I have a sister, but she left home at sixteen and I don't know where she is."

Keith said, "I'll go and make some phone calls."

Susan then asked Ellen if she had any sanitary towels – if so, could she have one and go to the bathroom? Ellen soon gave Susan a packet and told her where the bathroom was. When Susan came back, Ellen was holding Andy, who had woken up. His Babygro was wet as well as the blanket in his pushchair. Keith came back to talk to Susan while Ellen gave Andy a wash, changed him, then found a blanket and a clean Babygro. Andy seemed to love a bath and was soon clean and looking rather cute in a lemon Babygro with little cars on, and he smelt lovely. Keith had told Susan she could have a room in one of the better B & Bs; social services would sort out her benefits, but she wouldn't get any money for two weeks.

Susan began to panic. "I haven't got any food or anything for Andy. I'll use my savings and I'll be OK on bread and jam."

Keith said, "You'll do no such thing. I'll make a food parcel up for you. All you'll need is milk for a cup of tea. Ellen will sort everything you need for Andy – baby milk, nappies – and sanitary products for you, then you can choose some clothes for yourself."

Susan and Ellen were soon looking through clothes. Susan chose two skirts, three tops, three pairs of trousers, two dresses, two woollies, two pairs of shoes and a coat.

Ellen said, "Don't forget underwear – it's all brand new."

Bras and knickers were soon selected. Ellen had put six Babygros, three lovely little pairs of trousers and tops and three cardigans and socks in a bag along with two blankets for his pushchair. She also found a sleepsuit. It was a bit big, but he would grow into it. Nappies and sanitary products were also put in a bag. Keith in the meantime had made up two large bags of food.

Everything was taken up to the front room and put in the pushchair. Keith would take Susan to the B & B and carry little Andy.

When Susan saw how much there was she began to cry. "I don't know what to say. You've been so kind."

Keith said, "Come on, sweetheart – you get the pushchair; I'll bring Andy and we can go and find you a room. It's only five minutes away."

Susan hugged Ellen and she was gone.

When Keith came back he said that the room was lovely and clean with a single bed, cot, wardrobe, small fridge and television, also a small armchair. Susan loved it.

Keith and Ellen sat down for a cup of tea and Keith said, "Steve was right – that was a difficult one, and very sad. That dear little baby didn't ask to be born. Let's hope it's a new start for them. I'm shattered, are you?"

Ellen said, "You could say that."

They both knew that Susan wasn't unique. In fact, there were many, many more in very similar situations with no hope of anything better. Ellen went into the kitchen to get dinner ready. Thankfully the midnight patrol was quiet that night.

One very rare night when Keith and Ellen had a night off from the midnight patrol they decided to have an early night. They went up to bed and William followed. He got on the bed, kissed Keith and Ellen, and then lay down and died. Keith and Ellen cried uncontrollable, unstoppable tears – that little boy was so precious. Many would say he was just a dog, but many of you who are reading this and have fur babies of your own will know how they felt.

The weather was improving, so there were more homeless on the streets. Many of them wouldn't have it any other way. There were some you could help and others you couldn't for many different reasons, such as mental illness or sheer obstinacy. Keith and Ellen used to say in their prayers every day, "Thank You, Lord, for our home and someone to love. Bless all those who have no one and keep them safe." And they still continue to say that prayer every day.

In May Keith and Ellen were to attend the wedding of one of the children Ellen had been nanny to. It would be in North Walsham, so they would have a week's holiday and relax. It would do them both good. Although they would never admit it, they were both worn out.

A friend had said, "You two can't work all the hours you do and not feel shattered. You're not getting any younger. Sometimes you don't go to bed for days. Just be careful and think about yourselves for once."

Keith and Ellen knew the friend was right.

The wedding was lovely. The bride looked gorgeous, with three of the cutest bridesmaids in baby blue. The reception was very enjoyable. It had been a lovely day.

Keith and Ellen enjoyed the rest of the holiday, spent relaxing as usual. They stayed with Audrey and John, seeing Rene often. The holiday was soon over and it was back to Faith House and the old routine, but Keith had made the decision that they would have one night off from midnight patrol every two weeks, in the hope they wouldn't feel so tired.

Ellen and Keith felt that life had given them one or two blows lately. Ellen summed it up when she said, "Let's hope nothing else goes wrong."

Well, it did go wrong big time. Keith was told the work of the midnight patrol and street work was to finish. Keith asked why, but he was not given a reason. So he and Ellen would be out of a job and home in August. They could not believe they had been treated so badly, considering that Keith and Ellen had made contact with 56,000 people and helped 42,000 people. They were both incredulous. In all the years Keith and Ellen had been married, she had never seen him so angry and hurt.

Ellen was upset. She said, "Whatever will our young mums do? They won't cope without us."

Keith said, "Well, sweetheart, we can't do anything about it. We have to decide what we are going to do."

Lieutenant Colonel Eva came over. She was so supportive, but there was nothing she could do but listen.

Over the next few days Keith and Ellen made the decision as to what they would do. They looked at their financial situation and decided they would take a year out and rent a cottage in Norfolk. It just so happened that a friend of Audrey's had a cottage in North Walsham that he wanted to rent out, so Audrey arranged for Ellen to come up for the day to meet him and see the cottage. It was a lovely three-bedroom cottage with kitchen-diner, a nice bathroom and a lovely lounge with double doors out to the garden. Ellen paid the deposit and six months' rent and arranged a moving date for the end of August 1995. It was beautifully decorated, so Keith and Ellen could move straight in.

Audrey, John and Rene were delighted that Keith and Ellen were coming to live in North Walsham. Many of Keith's former RAF friends had retired in Norfolk and many of Ellen's lived in and around the town.

The move went smoothly. Audrey had gone down to the cottage to take delivery of the fridge-freezer and washing machine. When Keith and Ellen arrived Audrey and John were waiting for them. Audrey had got groceries in and had put milk and salad in the fridge along with ham and cheese. She had also stocked the freezer. The men soon emptied the van. Thankfully nothing had been damaged.

Once the men had gone everyone sat down with sandwiches for lunch. Audrey and John stayed for a while to help unpack. Keith and John unpacked downstairs while Audrey and Ellen unpacked upstairs and made the beds. The cottage soon began to look like home. At around 6.30 p.m. John ordered a takeaway for dinner, so they all decided to stop. Keith and Ellen would finish the unpacking the follow day.

Over the next few days everything was put in its place.

Ellen said, "Do you know, darling, it really feels like home. Are you happy?"

Keith said, "Yes, we've done the right thing."

Later they went into town to purchase a television, and as it was Thursday they would have a look in the market and afterwards they would pop into Rene's for coffee. Auntie Kathleen was there as she had now retired and lived in Aylsham, about eight miles from North Walsham. A few minutes after Keith and Ellen got there Audrey came, so everyone stopped and had a 'mardle' (a good old natter).

Over the next few months Keith and Ellen really began to relax and unwind, but their heads were still full of such knowledge that it seemed wicked that it wasn't being used. As it became known that Ellen was back in Norfolk, she had many requests for after-dinner speaking, and on many occasions she was asked if she would accept a donation for the Salvation Army. Ellen always said no, but she now supports a Third World children's organisation.

In November Ellen said one evening, "Won't it be strange not doing all the packages and parcels this year for Christmas?"

Ellen still did her Christmas cards early. She liked to post them at the end of November so they would arrive by the first Sunday in Advent.

Ellen and Keith's friends used to say, "Your card is always the first to arrive."

One particular friend said, "Why don't you send them in July to make sure we get them?"

So one year, just for fun, Ellen sent her friend's card in June.

At Christmas of 1995 the family would for the first time go to Ellen and Keith for Christmas lunch. During the first week in December Keith and Ellen decorated two Christmas trees – one for the lounge and one for the kitchen-diner. Keith put fairy lights all over the beams, in the windows and on the front door. When he had finished there were over 2,500 lights. The most important part of Christmas – the Nativity scene – was put in the alcove, and in the second week of December the wreath was put on the front door as a sign of welcome.

Christmas Day was lovely, although Rene missed Wilfred dreadfully. She looked so ill, but she kept cheerful.

At around 8.30 p.m. Rene said, "I'm rather tired, darlings. Would you mind if I go home?"

John got the car, and along with Audrey, Kathleen and Rene they left. It had been a lovely happy day.

CHAPTER 15

The snow fell heavily and it seemed it would never end, but it did look lovely. Getting round in rural Norfolk wasn't easy – snow chains were needed for the cars, *if* indeed you could get out! The freezer was full and somehow the milkman managed to get through, bringing milk, eggs and bread. Audrey and John were keeping an eye on Rene, and Ellen rang her every day. Ellen and Keith were only a mile from town and the gritters only did the main roads. It was so quiet and peaceful in Norfolk. The snow continued for another few weeks till at last it began to thaw, which made getting around much easier.

Over the next few months Rene became so unwell. She had seen various doctors and specialists, but there was nothing they could do. In July Rene went to heaven at the North Walsham Cottage Hospital.

Two days before she said to Keith, "I'm going to see my Wilfy tomorrow."

She had been riddled with cancer. Her funeral was held at the Salvation Army in North Walsham and she was laid to rest next to Wilfred. Keith and Ellen were given just two weeks to clear the flat.

As the weeks went by, life in Norfolk returned to normal. Late summer days were spent in the garden or by the coast. Audrey and John often came to Keith and Ellen, or when they were in town they would go down to Audrey's.

Ellen and Keith's friends had been to the cottage for lunch or dinner, and as another Christmas approached Audrey asked Ellen and Keith if they would like to go to her for Christmas Day.

The first few months of 1997 passed by, then one morning the phone rang and Ellen answered.

A voice said, "Good morning, Mrs Christian. How are you?"

Ellen said, "Very well, thank you."

The man said, "Is the boss there, please?"

Ellen said, "I'll give him a call. He's in the garden."

Keith came in, picked up the phone and said, "Good morning."

Ellen went to hang the washing on the line, and when she came back Keith was still on the phone.

After another forty minutes or so, Keith came into the kitchen and said, "Put the kettle on, love – we need to talk. Listen to everything I have to say, then tell me what you think."

Ellen sat and listened to what Keith said and could hardly believe what she heard. Keith had been headhunted for the position of house manager of a very prestigious apartment block in Grosvenor Square, Mayfair, London. Keith and Ellen would have an apartment in the block rent-free, all bills paid, and more money than they had ever seen. Moving expenses would also be paid. Keith would have a staff and have responsibility for the day-to-day running of the building.

The gentleman said, "Keith, you could do it with your eyes closed. Come and have a look and bring Ellen with you."

Keith said, "Can I ring you back when we've talked? I won't make the decision without Ellen."

When he had explained everything to Ellen Keith said, "What do you think, sweetheart?"

Ellen said, "I can hardly believe it. How do you feel?"

Keith said, "I think I would like to go and have a look. Would you be happy back in London? Grosvenor Square is a much better area."

Ellen said, "I'll be happy as long as we're together."

So that evening Keith and Ellen talked about the job and moving. The next morning a decision had been made, so Keith made the phone call to say that he and Ellen would like to see the apartment and learn more about the job, and a week later they got the train at 10 a.m. from Norwich to go to London. They had booked a room at the Victory Services Club, near Marble Arch, deciding to stay overnight so they would be on time for the interview the next morning. They would go and see a show that night.

When they arrived at Liverpool Street Station, they got a taxi to the club, and the next day at 11 a.m. they walked the short distance to Grosvenor Square and had a first glimpse of No. 7. It was an imposing building. The square itself was lovely, with plane trees, ponds and walkways.

As Keith and Ellen sat down for a few minutes, Keith said, "Isn't this nice? You wouldn't think we are only a two-minute walk from Oxford Street."

Ellen said, "Yes, it is nice. Now come on – we don't want to be late."

The interview went very well. Keith had sent his CV and references earlier, so the Residents Committee and the agent had them ready. At the end of the interview Keith was offered the job and Keith and Ellen were shown the apartment they would live in. The rooms were huge. You could have got the whole cottage in Norfolk in the lounge. It was lovely.

Keith was then asked, "What do you think, Mr Christian? Will you be our house manager?"

Keith said, "I would be delighted to accept."

He was then asked, "Can you start next week?"

Keith was a bit shocked.

Ellen said, "You could, love. I can pack home up in Norfolk."

So it was confirmed that Keith would start at Grosvenor Square the next week. Keith and Ellen were excited and nervous both at the same time, but they felt sure that it was the right decision. All they could talk about on the way home was their new home and Keith's job. Two very dear friends lived in London and were delighted that Keith and Ellen would be close by. They lent Keith a camp bed, bedding and pillows. Another friend lent him an armchair till Ellen had got everything packed for the move.

When Keith left for London, Ellen cried. She hated the thought of being apart. Even though it was for three weeks, it would seem like an eternity.

The next three weeks for Ellen were very busy. Audrey and John came to help with the packing, and at last it was done. The time came for Ellen to say goodbye to Audrey and John. It hurt, but she would come up once a month to see them.

Keith was waiting at Liverpool Street Station, and he told Ellen all the furniture, etc., had arrived the day before and he had started to unpack. They got home at around 5.30 p.m. and Keith had prepared a meal, so it wasn't long before they were sitting at the dining table for dinner.

They both slept well that night.

It was late August 1997. Keith settled into his house-manager role very well and worked each day till 2 p.m., and one weekend in three. The apartment block inside was beautiful, with marble staircases. In the foyer was an amazing crystal chandelier.

Ellen began to meet the residents, and many of them were lovely and friendly. As promised, Ellen went up to Norfolk once a month for two days. They both continued to attend some wonderful functions, such as Beating the Retreat on Horse Guards Parade in the presence of Her Majesty the Queen, and a visit to the Magic Circle. No matter how closely you looked it was impossible to work out how the various tricks were done.

The first Christmas at No. 7 Ellen decorated a Christmas tree and put it in the foyer. It was a green tree with white lights and deep-red and gold decorations. It looked superb and was a great success, so it was put up each year thereafter. One evening Lieutenant Colonel Stan and Eva came for dinner, and they thought everything was lovely. Many of Keith and Ellen's other friends came to visit too.

One of them said, "Oh my, this is posh."

Keith and Ellen smiled, but she was right.

Some of their friends in Norfolk laughingly said, "Don't you get ideas above your station, my woman."

Keith loved his job, and Ellen too enjoyed being in London. She felt safe going out alone. It was so very different to King's Cross. The American Embassy was opposite No. 7, so security in the square was very good. Almost every morning the King's Troop, Royal Horse Artillery, would go past No. 7 with their gun carriages. It was a wonderful sight.

Another colourful event that went through the square was the Gay Pride March. Some of the costumes were really lovely. It was great fun to watch.

Another event which could only happen in London caused quite a lot of amusement – around 400 men and women completely naked on bicycles riding around the square. It was the ride to claim back the streets for cyclists. Certainly a sight you wouldn't see in Norfolk!

It hardly seemed possible, but the millennium was approaching.

Although there were many wonderful celebrations in and around London, Keith and Ellen preferred to stay at home. However, they did go on to the roof of No. 7 to watch the fireworks over the Thames. It was a magical sight.

In April 2000 Ellen was taken poorly and had to go into hospital. She had a three-and-a-half-stone fibroid removed and had to have a hysterectomy as well. Ellen soon bounced back. A month later Keith and Ellen had a two-week holiday in Derbyshire and Norfolk.

In September 2001, on a day no one will ever forget, two aircraft crashed into the Twin Towers of the World Trade Center on Manhattan Island, New York, killing so many innocent people. The next few days after the tragedy Grosvenor Square was a sea of floral tributes, from a single red rose to the very intricate Stars and Stripes flag and many others in between. It was a very emotive sight. There were hundreds of visitors in the square every day, but it was eerily quiet. A book of condolence was opened up in a marquee in the square, and later a memorial garden was created within the square. All the names of those who died were engraved on a wall. It was very moving reading it.

In 2002 Keith and Ellen went to the Isle of Wight for a holiday, staying with Keith's sister, Dawn, and had a lovely week. On the way back they went to stay with Audrey and John.

One day they took Audrey and Auntie Kathleen out for the day, and one of the places they visited was Alby Crafts, where there were lovely little shops selling all sorts of handmade things – pottery, stained glass, cards and paper craft. There was also wool and haberdashery and an art gallery, to name but a few. It was a lovely day.

The next day Kathleen was to go on a two-week holiday to Holland with a friend. She loved Holland and went every year, sometimes twice.

Keith and Ellen returned home to London, and on 12 June 2002 John rang to say Kathleen had returned from holiday, got off the coach at Norwich, collapsed and went to heaven instantly. It was such a shock as she had been so fit. It turned out to be a blood clot that had travelled to her heart.

On the 14th Ellen travelled up to Norfolk to help Audrey with all the arrangements for the funeral and to clear Kathleen's bungalow. Two weeks later Kathleen's funeral was held at the Salvation Army in Coltishall and she was buried in Aylsham Cemetery.

On 28 June Ellen returned to London, the day before her fiftieth birthday. Keith took Ellen to dinner at the Window on the World Restaurant at the Hilton, Park Lane. She later said that she had felt like royalty.

Another guild function Keith and Ellen won't forget was dinner at the Goldsmiths' Hall. Ellen had a beautiful new blue evening gown and Keith looked so smart in his evening suit. The hall was incredible. The dining hall had huge chandeliers lit by many, many real candles. It certainly was a sight to behold. When everyone had been seated, dinner was served.

All was going well – guests were chatting to each other – when all of a sudden the lady opposite Keith shouted, "Keith, move!"

But it was too late. The glass of the chandelier Keith was sitting under had shattered, spilling extremely hot wax over his hand and face and on to his jacket. Thankfully his beard stopped his face being burnt, but his right hand was burnt quiet badly. He was given immediate medical attention. It soon got round the hall that Keith had been hurt. When he came back in it was to applause from the guests. The Master of Goldsmiths was very apologetic. It had never happened before. It took many weeks for Keith's hand to heal completely.

As time went by life for Keith and Ellen was wonderful. In 2003 two darling little six-week-old West Highland puppies came into their lives – Barnaby and Rupert. They were brothers from the same litter, and just adorable. It soon became clear they had totally different personalities. Rupert was so laid-back and craved cuddles and loved to play. He loved everyone he met. Barnaby was more aloof and would love people on his terms.

Once they had been given their injections and were allowed to go for a walk, they loved going into Grosvenor Square and also to Hyde Park, although you sometimes had to carry them home as they refused to go any further – after all, they were only little.

One day after lunch when the boys were about eighteen months old Keith took them for a walk in the square.

He came back indoors and said, "A strange lady followed me all the way round the square."

Ellen said, "Don't worry, love – I expect she's harmless."

It happened again the next day and the next.

On the following afternoon's walk as Keith got level with the Millennium Hotel the same lady shouted from a bedroom window, "Hello. Hello." She ran into the square and said in a very broad American accent, "I'm Jo. I've been waiting for you to go past."

Keith said, "Oh, hello."

Jo then said, "Can I talk to your Westies? I'm on holiday with my husband, Don. We're from Connecticut, in the States, and we've got two Westies and I miss them."

Keith said laughingly, "So you're my stalker."

Jo also laughed.

Over the next week she waited every day and looked out for Keith and the boys, and over the years she and Don became friends with Keith and Ellen.

Keith and Ellen still enjoyed being in London, with Keith enjoying his job at No. 7. The two of them had trips to the theatre and guild functions; friends came to stay and enjoyed London too.

Time seemed to travel on so quickly. Weeks turned into months and months into years. In 2009 Ellen became very unwell once more, but no one could say why. She had numerous tests, but nothing was found. Keith was worried and asked the Doctor if he could take Ellen away for a two-week holiday in Norfolk in late April.

The Doctor said, "Yes, but as we don't know what the problem is Ellen must rest."

So they went to stay with Audrey and John with Barnaby and Rupert.

Audrey said to Keith, "Have you had a second opinion?"

Keith said, "Yes, but nothing has been found."

When Keith and Ellen got back to London there was an urgent message on the answerphone for Ellen to contact the Doctor asap.

Ellen rang and the Doctor said, "I need you to come and see me now. Bring Keith with you."

It frightened Ellen. They went to see him. Apparently an earlier scan had been looked at again by a medical student, and a mass had been found. No one knew what it was, so Ellen would need an ultrasound scan that day.

The Doctor said, "I will meet you both at the hospital in an hour."

Keith, Ellen and the Doctor went into the ultrasound room and Ellen was told she would need an emergency operation to remove the mass, but still no one could say what it was.

The Doctor said to Keith, "We need to get this done quickly. Ellen's life is in danger."

Keith said, "When does she need the operation?"

The Doctor said, "Now, but there's a wait. However, Keith, there is an option to go private. In that case I could get Ellen into hospital in the morning."

Keith said, "OK, Doc. How much will it cost?"

Keith was told £18,000.

Keith said, "OK, make the arrangements. Which hospital do I have to get Ellen to?"

The Doctor said, "The Princess Grace Hospital in Marylebone."

So the next morning at 8.30 a.m. Ellen entered the hospital and at 4.20 p.m. she went down to the theatre, telling the surgeon she was in God's hands. At 7.45 p.m. the hospital rang Keith to tell him Ellen was in intensive care. They had found a massive staghorn stone that had torn a hole in Ellen's bowel. Eighteen inches had to be removed. It had also infected a kidney, which was also removed along with her spleen. She was extremely poorly, but Keith was allowed in to see her for ten minutes. He cried when he saw Ellen. She was sedated, but she knew he was there.

The Nurse said, "You can come back tomorrow for a short while. We will look after Ellen."

They nearly lost her twice in the night, but in the morning Ellen woke up and asked for a cup of tea. When Keith came she was able to speak a little, but was still very weak.

Keith left after thirty minutes promising to be back the next day. The next morning Ellen managed a slice of toast and a cup of tea and soup for lunch. When Keith arrived she had been moved to her own room. It was like a five-star hotel, with a lovely armchair by the bed, an en-suite bathroom and toilet, and a television and radio. The food was lovely and at 11 a.m. every morning coffee and biscuits were brought to her room. At 3 p.m. tea and cake were served.

Ellen got stronger as the days went by, and on the eighth day she was allowed home. A nurse would go in twice a day to dress the wound. Ellen had a twenty-two-inch scar with eighty staples and fifty stitches. It was very tender. The nurse who came in every day was lovely, kind and gentle, especially when an abscess developed on the wound. Eva came to visit, as did other friends. Ellen received over 300 get-well cards and letters, and the apartment looked like a florist's shop. The perfume from the flowers was amazing.

Ellen slowly began to improve with Keith's wonderful love and care till at 3 a.m. one morning Ellen woke to find the bed wet. The wound had burst open and was leaking badly.

Keith said, "OK, love, don't move. I'll ring the Doctor."

The Doctor said he was on the way, and half an hour later he was with Ellen.

He said, "Oh, my love, you are in a mess. I daren't move you. I'll have to stitch you up here. Will you be OK? I'll be as quick as I can, but it's going to hurt. Are you ready?"

Ellen said, "Yes."

Keith held her hand and the Doctor was right – it did b----- hurt.

When he had finished he said, "I'll be back in the morning. Don't you dare get out of bed until I get back."

The next morning the Doctor came back with the Nurse.

Ellen said, "Can I go to the loo, please?"

He said, "Yes, with the Nurse's help. Then you can lie on the sofa."

He gave the Nurse new instructions for dressing the wound, now three times a day. He was worried about infection. All in all it took a full six months to the day for the wound to heal.

An RAF friend said to Keith, "I hope you're going to sue for negligence."

Keith said, "No – I just thank God I've still got my Ellen."

At the Lord Mayor's Banquet Keith and Ellen were privileged to be presented to HRH the Princess Royal – something they will never forget. They have two wonderful photos as mementos of the occasion.

In March 2011 Keith retired and Ellen, Keith, Barnaby and Rupert went to live in Norfolk. They were only a five-minute walk from Audrey and John. Ellen liked nothing more than looking at the stars in the night sky – something she couldn't do in London due to light pollution.

In October Keith said, "I need something to do, darling."

So he applied for a Christmas job on the checkouts at Sainsbury's in North Walsham. He got the job and loved it. It was part-time. After Christmas Keith was asked if he would like to stay on, and he said yes, so Keith did part-time at Sainsbury's while Ellen took up card making and crochet. She took orders for one-off cards, all the money going to charity.

In July 2012 John became very ill with cancer. He went to heaven at home with Audrey by his side in mid October. His funeral was at the Salvation Army and he was buried in the cemetery.

In November Don and Jo came over to Norfolk and stayed with Ellen and Keith.

In early 2013 two very special people came into Keith and Ellen's lives – Pat and Kevin, the kindest most caring couple you could find. They would do anything for Keith and Ellen and have taken them into their family with so much love being given. Keith and Ellen feel truly blessed.

In 2015 Keith and Ellen were thrilled to be asked to be 'Nana' and 'Papa' to a darling little boy. He brings so much joy into their lives. He is so full of life and wonderful mischief. His lovely mummy and daddy are bringing him up to be a polite little boy, who we know will develop into a lovely young man.

CHAPTER 16

2016 began cold and crisp. The weatherman said that snow was on the way, and sure enough it arrived at the end of January; but thankfully it didn't last long. Auntie Audrey became very confused and angry. She would forget where things were and ring Keith and Ellen at all times of the day and night. She began to say things that if she knew what she was saying she would have been horrified. It was clear she was becoming unsafe to live alone, but she refused any form of help and was soon diagnosed with dementia. Ellen and Keith took it all in their stride, agreeing with all she said and listening to the same tale over and over again. They laughed about some of the things she did and said. It was no good being uptight about the situation. The Auntie Audrey Ellen had grown up with had gone – there was nothing anyone could do about it. Oh, Ellen still loved Audrey very much, but some days she didn't like her. On 21 April 2016 Ellen and Keith went down to visit Audrey, as they did every day, and found she had gone to heaven while sitting in her armchair. She looked so peaceful.

Two weeks earlier she had said to Keith, "When I go to heaven I want to go to sleep in my armchair and not wake up."

The Lord had granted her wish.

Audrey's funeral was at the Salvation Army and she was buried with her John.

Keith and Ellen's fortieth (ruby) wedding anniversary, on 1 May 2016, was a wonderful occasion. A lunch for fifty friends and family was held at Scarborough Hill Country Inn in North

Walsham. Keith's sister and two brothers were there with their respective partners, as were Lieutenant Colonel Stan and Eva, Keith's best man and the other people Keith and Ellen loved the most. Ellen said in her speech that she and Keith could feel the love in the room that day. She also said that she and Keith felt their lives had been truly blessed, not only because of the love they had for each other, but also for the love of true friends.

Ellen said, "True friends are like stars: you don't always see them, but you know they are always there."

God's love has been with Keith and Ellen in all they have done – in the good times and the not so good. His love is everlasting.

So we come to the end of our story. Who knows what the future will hold? But one thing is for sure: with God's love and each other they can face anything.

Many people have come into Keith and Ellen's lives over the years, and many have influenced them in different ways – parents, teachers, Grandy, Keith's grandparents, aunties, uncles, brothers and sister and many friends. Love has played a huge part, and here Ellen would like to say a heartfelt thank you to all of those who have loved her and Keith without question. Many times you have said three very special words that mean so much: "I love you." Keith and Ellen hope you will know how very much they love you too.

GOD BLESS YOU.